Course **General Microbiology**

Course Number **BIOL 211**

Ivy Tech.Lafayette

http://create.mcgraw-hill.com

ISBN-10: 0390646105   ISBN-13: 9780390646101

Contents

Credits

BASIC MICROBIOLOGY
LABORATORY SAFETY

Every student and instructor must focus on the need for safety in the microbiology laboratory. While the lab is a fascinating and exciting learning environment, there are hazards that must be acknowledged and rules that must be followed to prevent accidents and contamination with microbes. The following outline will provide every member of the laboratory section the information required to assure a safe learning environment.

The "Biohazard" symbol must be affixed to any container or equipment used to store or transport potentially infectious materials.

Courtesy of the Centers for Disease Control.

Microbiological laboratories are special, often unique environments that may pose identifiable infectious disease risks to persons who work in or near them. Infections have been contacted in the laboratory throughout the history of microbiology. Early reports described laboratory-associated cases of typhoid, cholera, glanders, brucellosis, and tetanus to name a few. Recent reports have documented laboratory-acquired cases in laboratory workers and health-care personnel involving *Bacillus anthrasis, Bordetella pertusis, Brucella, Burkholderia pseudomallei, Campylobacter, Chlamydia,* and toxins from *Clostridium tetani, Clostridium botulinum,* and *Corynebacterium diphtheriae.* While we have a greater knowledge of these agents and antibiotics with which to treat them, safety and handling still remain primary issues.

The term "containment" is used to describe the safe methods and procedures for handling and managing microorganisms in the laboratory. An important laboratory procedure practiced by all microbiologists that will guarantee containment is **aseptic technique,** which prevents workers from contaminating themselves with microorganisms, ensures that others and the work area do not become contaminated, and also ensures that microbial cultures do not become unnecessarily contaminated with unwanted organisms. Primary containment involves personnel and the immediate laboratory and is provided by good microbiological technique and use of appropriate safety equipment. Secondary containment is also important because it guarantees that infectious agents do not escape from the laboratory and contaminate the environment external to the lab. Containment, therefore, relies on good microbiological technique and laboratory protocol as well as elements of laboratory design.

Biosafety Levels (BSL)

The recommended biosafety level(s) for handling microorganisms represent the potential of the agent to cause disease and the conditions under which the agent should be safely handled. The Centers for Disease Control recommends biosafety levels for microorganisms and viruses. These levels take into account many factors such as virulence, pathogenicity, antibiotic resistance patterns, vaccine and treatment availability, and other factors. The recommended biosafety levels are as follows:

1. **BSL 1**—agents not known to cause disease in healthy adults; standard microbiological practices (SMP) apply; no safety equipment required; sinks required. Examples: *Bacillus subtilis, Micrococcus lutetus*
2. **BSL 2**—agents associated with human disease; standard microbiological practices apply plus limited access, biohazard signs, sharps precautions, and a biosafety manual required. Biosafety cabinet (BSC) used for aerosol/splash generating operations; lab coats, gloves, face protection required; contaminated waste is autoclaved. **All microorganisms used in the exercises in this manual are classified as BSL 1 or BSL 2.** Examples: *Staphylococcus aureus, Streptococcus pyogenes*

Note: Although some of the organisms that students will culture and work with are classified as BSL 2, these organisms are laboratory strains that do not pose the same threat of infection as primary isolates of the same organism taken from patients in clinical samples. Hence, these laboratory strains can, in most cases, be handled using normal procedures and equipment found in the vast majority of student teaching laboratories. However, it should be emphasized that many bacteria are opportunistic pathogens and therefore all microorganisms should be handled by observing proper techniques and precautions.

3. **BSL 3**—indigenous/exotic agents that may have serious or lethal consequences and with a potential for aerosol transmission. BSL 2 practices plus controlled access; decontamination of all waste and lab clothing before laundering; determination of baseline antibody titers to agents; biosafety cabinets used for all specimen manipulations; respiratory protection used as needed; physical separation from access corridors; double door access; negative airflow into the lab; exhaust air not recirculated. Examples: *Mycobacterium tuberculosis* and vesicular stomatitis virus (VSV)
4. **BSL 4**—dangerous/exotic agents of a life-threatening nature or unknown risk of transmission; BSL 3 practices plus clothing change before

entering the laboratory; shower required before leaving the lab; all materials decontaminated on exit; positive pressure personnel suit required for entry; separated/isolated building; dedicated air supply/exhaust and decontamination systems. Examples: Ebola and Lassa viruses

Each of the biosafety levels consist of combinations of laboratory practices and techniques, safety equipment and laboratory facilities. Each combination is specifically appropriate for the operations performed and the documented or suspected routes of transmission of the infectious agents. Common to all biosafety levels are standard practices, especially aseptic technique.

Standard Laboratory Rules and Practices

1. Students should store all books and materials not used in the laboratory in areas or receptacles designated for that purpose. Only a lab notebook, the laboratory manual, and pen/pencil should be brought to the student work area.
2. Eating, drinking, chewing gum, and smoking are not allowed in the laboratory. Students must also avoid handling contact lenses or applying make-up while in the laboratory.
3. Safety equipment:
   a. Some labs will require that lab coats be worn in the laboratory at all times. Others may make this optional or not required. Lab coats can protect a student from contamination by microorganisms that he/she is working with and prevent contamination from stains and chemicals. At the end of the laboratory session, lab coats are usually stored in the lab in a manner prescribed by the instructor. Lab coats, gloves, and safety equipment should not be worn outside of the laboratory unless properly decontaminated first.
   b. You may be required to wear gloves while performing the lab exercises. They protect the hands against contamination by microorganisms and prevent the hands from coming in direct contact with stains and other reagents.
   c. Face protection/safety glasses may be required by some instructors while you are performing experiments. Safety glasses can prevent materials from coming in contact with the eyes. They must be especially worn when working with ultraviolet light to prevent eye damage because they block out UV rays. If procedures involve the potential for splash/aerosols, face protection should be worn.
   d. Know the location of eye wash and shower stations in the event of an accident that requires

the use of this equipment. Also know the location of first aid kits.

4. Sandals or open-toe shoes are not be worn in the laboratory. Accidental dropping of objects could result in serious injury.
5. Students with long hair should tie the hair back to avoid accidents when working with Bunsen burners/open flames. Long hair can also be a source of contamination when working with cultures.
6. Before beginning the activities for the day, work areas should be wiped down with the disinfectant that is provided for that purpose. Likewise, when work is finished for the day, the work area should be treated with disinfectant to ensure that any contamination from the exercise performed is destroyed. Aviod contamination of the work surface by not placing contaminated pipettes, loops/needles, or swabs on the work surface. Dispose of contaminated paper towels used for swabbing in the biohazard container.
7. Use extreme caution when working with open flames. The flame on a Bunsen burner is often difficult to see when not in use. Caution is imperative when working with alcohol and open flames. Alcohol is highly flammable and fires can easily result when using glass rods that have been dipped in alcohol. **Always make sure the gas is turned off before leaving the laboratory.**
8. Any cuts or injuries on the hands must be covered with band-aids to prevent contamination. If you injure or cut yourself during the laboratory, notify the laboratory instructor immediately.
9. Pipetting by mouth is prohibited in the lab. All pipetting must be performed with pipette-aids. Be especially careful when inserting glass pipettes into pipette aids as the pipette can break and cause a serious injury.
10. Know the location of exits and fire extinguishers in the laboratory.
11. Most importantly, read the exercise and understand the laboratory protocol before coming to laboratory. In this way you will be familiar with potential hazards in the exercise.
12. When working with microfuges, be familiar with their safe operation and make sure that all microfuge tubes are securely capped before centrifuging.
13. When working with electrophoresis equipment, follow the directions carefully to aviod electric shock.
14. If you have any allergies or medical conditions that might be complicated by participating in the laboratory, inform the instructor. Women who are pregnant should discuss the matter of enrolling in the lab with their family physician and the laboratory instructor.

▌ BASIC MICROBIOLOGY LABORATORY SAFETY

Disposal of Biological Wastes

Dispose of all contaminated materials properly and in the appropriate containers:

1. Biohazard containers—biohazard containers are to be lined with clear autoclave bags; disposable petri plates, used gloves, and any materials such as contaminated paper towels, etc., should be discarded in these containers; no glassware, test tubes, or sharp items are to disposed of in biohazard containers.
2. Sharpkeepers—sharps, slides, coverslips, broken glass, disposable pipettes, and Pasteur pipettes should be discarded in these containers. If instructed to do so, you can discard contaminated swabs, wooden sticks, and microfuge tubes in the sharpkeepers.
3. Discard shelves, carts, etc.—contaminated culture tubes and glassware used to store media and other glassware should be placed in these areas for decontamination and washing.
4. Trash cans—any noncontaminated materials, paper, or trash should be discarded in these containers. Under no circumstances should laboratory waste should be disposed of in trash cans.

Discard other materials as directed by your instructor. This may involve placing materials such as slides contaminated with blood in disinfectant baths before these materials can be discarded.

Emergencies

Surface Contamination

1. Report all spills immediately to the laboratory instructor.
2. Cover the spill with paper towels and saturate the paper towels with disinfectant.
3. Allow the disinfectant to act for at least 20 minutes.
4. Remove any glass or solid material with forceps or scoop and discard the waste in an appropriate manner.

Personnel Contamination

1. Notify lab instructor.
2. Clean exposed area with soap/water, eye wash (eyes) or saline (mouth).
3. Apply first aid and treat as an emergency.

Microbiology, 11th Edition,
Short Version

BASIC MICROBIOLOGY LABORATORY SAFETY ▌

Biosafety Levels for Selected Infectious Agents

Biosafety Level (BSL)	Typical Risk	Organism
BSL 1	Not likely to pose a disease risk to healthy adults.	*Achromobacter denitrificans* *Alcaligenes faecalis* *Bacillus cereus* *Bacillus subtilis* *Corynebacterium pseudodiphtheriticum* *Enterobacter aerogenes* *Enterococcus faecalis* *Micrococcus luteus* *Neisseria sicca* *Proteus vulgaris* *Pseudomonas aeruginosa* *Staphylococcus epidermidis* *Staphylococcus saprophyticus*
BSL 2	Poses a moderate risk to healthy adults; unlikely to spread throughout community; effective treatment readily available.	*Escherichia coli* *Klebsiella pneumoniae* *Mycobacterium phlei* *Salmonella enterica var. Typhimurium* *Shigella flexneri* *Staphylococcus aureus* *Streptococcus pneumoniae* *Streptococcus pyogenes*
BSL 3	Can cause disease in healthy adults; may spread to community; effective treatment readily available.	*Blastomyces dermatitidis* *Chlamydia trachomatis* *Coccidioides immitis* *Coxiella burnetii* *Francisella tularensis* *Histoplasma capsulatum* *Mycobacterium bovis* *Mycobacterium tuberculosis* *Pseudomonas mallei* *Rickettsia canadensis* *Rickettsia prowazekii* *Yersinia pestis*
BSL 4	Can cause disease in healthy adults; poses a lethal risk and does not respond to vaccines or antimicrobial therapy.	*Filovirus* *Herpesvirus simiae* Lassa virus Marburg virus

Microbiology, 11th Edition,
Short Version

Microorganisms Used or Isolated in the Lab Exercises in this Manual

Organism	Gram Stain and Morphology	Habitat	BSL	Lab Exercise
Alcaligenes faecalis ATCC 19018	Negative rod	Decomposing organic material, feces	1	31
Azotobacter insignis ATCC 12523	Negative rod	Soil, water	1	52
Azotobacter nigricans ATCC 35009	Negative rod	Soil, water	1	52
Azotobacter vinelandii ATCC 12518	Negative rod	Soil, water	1	52
Bacillus cereus var. mycoides ATCC 21929	Positive rod in chains	Soil	1	59
Bacillus coagulans ATCC 10778	Positive rod	Spoiled food, silage	1	64
Bacillus megaterium ATCC 35985	Positive rod	Soil, water	1	13, 15, 16, 19, 30, 33
Bacillus subtilis ATCC 31578	Positive rod	Soil, decomposing organic matter	1	16, 21, 42
Candida glabrata ATCC 200918	Yeast	Human oral cavity	1	31
Chromobacterium violaceum ATCC 12572	Negative rod	Soil and water; opportunistic pathogen in humans	1	10
Citrobacter freundii ATCC 8090	Negative rod	Humans, animals, soil water; sewage opportunistic pathogen	1	72
Clostridium beijerinckii ATCC 14949	Positive rod	Soil	1	21
Clostridium sporogenes ATCC 10000	Positive rod	Soil, animal feces	1	21, 57, 64
Corynebacterium xerosis ATCC 373	Positive rods, club-shaped	Conjunctiva, skin	1	12
Desulfovibrio desulfuricans ATCC 13541	Negative, curved rods	Soil, sewage, water	1	56
Enterobacter aerogenes ATCC 29007	Positive cocci, occur in chains	Feces of man and animals	2	21
Enterococcus faecium ATCC 19433	Positive cocci in pairs, short chains	Feces of humans and animals	2	71
Enterococcus faecalis ATCC 10741	Negative rods	Water, sewage, soil, dairy products	2	41, 43, 61
Escherichia coli ATCC 31446	Negative rods	Sewage, intestinal tract of warm-blooded animals	2	9, 19, 21, 22, 26, 27, 29, 30, 31, 34, 36, 41, 42, 58, 59, 61, 64, 66, 67, 68

Microbiology, 11th Edition,
Short Version

BASIC MICROBIOLOGY LABORATORY SAFETY ▮

Microorganisms Used or Isolated in the Lab Exercises in this Manual (continued)

Organism	Gram Stain and Morphology	Habitat	BSL	Lab Exercise
Geobacillus stearothermophilus ATCC 12976	Variable rods	Soil, spoiled food	1	64
Halobacterium salinarium ATCC 19700	Gives gram-negative reaction; rods	Salted fish, hides, meats	1	32
Klebsiella pneumoniae ATCC 10273	Negative rods	Intestinal tract of humans; respiratory and intestinal pathogen in humans	2	14
Micrococcus luteus ATCC 12698	Positive cocci that occur in pairs	Mammalian skin	1	18, 78
Moraxella (Branhamella) catarrhalis ATCC 232446	Negative cocci that often occur in pairs with flattened sides	Pharynx of humans	1	15
Mycobacterium smegmatis ATCC 14468	Positive rods; may be **Y**-shaped or branched	Smegma of humans	1	15, 17
Paracoccus denitrificans ATCC 15543	Negative spherical cells or short rods	Soil	1	53
Penicillium chrysogenum ATCC 9478	Filamentous fungus	Soil	1	59
Physarum polycephalum ATCC 204388	Slime mold	Decaying leaves	1	23
Proteus vulgaris ATCC 12454	Negative rods	Intestines of humans, and animals; soil and polluted waters	1	18, 36, 42, 43, 58
Pseudomonas aeruginosa ATCC 47053	Negative rods	Soil and water; opportunistic pathogen in humans	1	15, 36, 37, 41
Pseudomonas fluorescens ATCC 11150	Negative rods	Soil, water, spoiled food; clinical specimens	1	59
Saccharomyces cerevisiae ATCC 76455	Yeast		1	31
Salmonella enterica subsp. enterica serovar *Typhimurium* ATCC 35988	Negative rods	Most frequent agent of *Salmonella* gastroenteritis in humans	2	73
Serratia marcescens ATCC 13880	Negative rods	Opportunistic pathogen in humans	1	
Shigella flexneri ATCC 29903	Negative rods	Pathogen of humans	2	72
Staphylococcus aureus ATCC 35556	Positive cocci, irregular clusters	Skin, nose, GI tract of humans, pathogen	2	10, 13, 15, 17, 21, 28, 30, 31, 33 34, 36, 37, 41, 42 43, 57, 58, 59, 70 71, 73
Staphylococcus epidermidis ATCC 155	Positive cocci that occur in pairs and tetrads	Human skin, animals; opportunistic pathogen	1	49, 70

**Microbiology, 11th Edition,
Short Version**

Microorganisms Used or Isolated in the Lab Exercises in this Manual

Organism	Gram Stain and Morphology	Habitat	BSL	Lab Exercise
Staphylococcus saprophyticus ATCC 15305	Positive cocci that occur singly and in pairs	Human skin; opportunistic pathogen in the urinary tract	1	70
Streptococcus agalactiae ATCC 14364	Positive cocci; occurs in long chains	Upper respiratory and vaginal tract of humans, cattle; pathogen	2	71
Streptococcus bovis ATCC 35034	Positive cocci; pairs and chains	Cattle, sheep, pigs; occasional pathogen in humans	2	71
Streptococcus dysagalactiae subspecies *equisimilis* ATCC 35666	Positive cocci; short to long chains	mastitis in cattle	2	71
Streptococcus equi ATCC 39506	Positive cocci; cocco-bacilli; occur in pairs and chains	Pathogen of horses	2	71
Streptococcus mitis ATCC 49456	Positive cocci in pairs and chains	Oral cavity of humans	2	71
Streptococcus mutans ATCC 33402	Positive cocci in pairs and chains	Tooth surface of humans, causes dental caries	2	71
Streptococcus pneumoniae ATCC 10015	Positive cocci in pairs	Human pathogen	2	71
Streptococcus pyogenes ATCC 12202	Positive cocci in chains	Human respiratory tract; pathogen	2	71
Streptococcus salivarius ATCC 25975	Positive cocci in short and long chains	Tongue and saliva	2	71
Thermoanaerobacterium thermosaccharolyticum ATCC 7965	Negative rods; single cells or pairs	Soil, spoiled canned foods	1	64

PREFACE

Benson's Microbial Applications has been the "gold standard" of microbiology laboratory manuals for over 30 years. This manual has a number of attractive features that resulted in its adoption in universities, colleges, and community colleges for a wide variety of microbiology courses. These features include "user friendly" diagrams that students can easily follow, clear instructions, and an excellent array of reliable exercises suitable for beginning or advanced microbiology courses.

In revising the tenth edition, I have tried to maintain these important strengths and further enhance the manual by updating exercises and making the bacterial nomenclature more consistent with the first edition of *Bergey's Manual of Systematic Bacteriology*. The second edition of *Bergey's Manual* is in publication but is incomplete at this time.

Organizational Changes

Changes to the 11th edition include:

- The safety rules have been rewritten to be more consistent with rules and regulations that apply to student laboratories.
- A new table of the organisms used in the manual has been introduced. The table includes the current accepted name of the organism, its ATCC number, Gram stain and morphology, its habitat, its biosafety level, and the exercise in which the organism is used.
- The exercises on the protozoa and algae (Exercise 5) and the fungi (Exercise 7) in the Survey of Microorganisms have been revised. The new exercises have been updated with the current taxonomy of these two groups of microorganisms.
- The existing photographs of the simple, acid-fast, Gram, capsule, and spore stains in Part 2, Survey of Microorganisms, have been replaced with new photos. Also, a new photo of a negative stain has been added.
- The introductory material in Exercise 19, Cultivation of Anaerobes, has been expanded to include a revised listing of organisms and a discussion of how oxygen affects different groups of bacteria. The discussion also includes comments on the nature of sensitivity of anaerobes to oxygen.
- Exercise 31 on The Effects of Lysozyme on Bacterial Cells has been revised. The new exercise includes an expanded discussion on wall structure and the role of teichoic acids in the gram-positive bacterial cell wall. The exercise also includes testing human saliva as a source of lysozyme. The effects of lysozyme on gram-positive and negative cells are discussed and how the presence of

teichoic acids in the cell wall of *Staphylococcus aureus* inhibits the action of lysozyme.
- The table on antimicrobic disks in Exercise 33, Antimicrobic Sensitivity Testing, has been expanded to include more antimicrobics. Also included are the potency values for each antimicrobic disk and specific values for sensitive, intermediate, and resistant categories for various organisms. The introductory material now includes definitions for antibiotics, antimicrobics, and semi-synthetic and synthetic compounds.
- Figures and flow charts in Exercises 38 and 39 for the identification of an unknown have been revised and modified to make them more easy to follow.
- The introductory material in Exercise 46, Bacterial Counts of Food, has been expanded. This section now includes a discussion on the association of bacteria with foods. It also addresses how foods are important in foodborne diseases and how counts may or not be important in transmission of disease.
- The introductory section of Exercise 55, Slide Agglutination Test, has been expanded to include a more detailed discussion of antigens and the antibody response.

Laboratory Reports

The laboratory reports are designed to guide and reinforce student learning and provide a convenient place for recording data. The reports consist of observation sections, results sections, short answer questions, multiple-choice questions, and fill-in-the-blank questions. Instructors may choose to either post the answer key from the instructor's manual so students can check their work or collect and grade the laboratory reports.

Instructor's Manual

The accompanying instructor's manual provides: (1) a listing of equipment and supplies needed for performing all of the experiments, (2) procedures for setting up the experiments, and (3) answers to all the questions for the laboratory reports. The instructor's manual can be found at www.mhhe.com/labcentral. Please contact your sales representative for additional information.

Acknowledgements

I want to express my deep gratitude to Dr. Kathy Lawrence and Dr. Christine Sundermann of Auburn University for revising the exercises on fungi and protozoa and algae respectively.

Microbiology, 11th Edition,
Short Version

PREFACE ▌

I would also like to thank Dr. Mike Miller, Director of the Auburn University Research Instrumentation Facility for photographing the various stains in Part 4, Staining and Observation of Micro-organisms.

I would also like to thank Georgeann Ellis, Coordinator of the Microbiology laboratories at Auburn University who made corrections to the manual and many helpful suggestions.

Sang-Jin Suh from Auburn University provided me with invaluable input on the bacterial genetics and biotechnology exercises.

I also want to extend thanks to Barry Chess from Pasadena City College for updating the instructor's manual.

I wish to express my utmost gratitude to Dr. Jolie Stepaniak for reviewing each exercise in the manual and making many helpful recommendations that helped improve the 11th edition.

The updates and improvements in this edition were guided by the helpful reviews of the following instructors. Their input was critical to the decisions that shaped this edition of *Benson's Microbiological Applications.*

Mohammed K. Abbas *Schoolcraft College*
Raj Boopathy *Nicholls State University*
Marc A. Brodkin *Widener University*
Paula J. Burns *Mendocino Community College*
Barry Chess *Pasadena City College*
Neena Din *Loyola College*
David W. Essar *Winona State University*

Allen Lee Farrand *Bellevue Community College*
K. Michael Foos *Indiana University East*
Denise Y. Friedman *Hudson Valley Community College*
Phillip E. Funk *DePaul University*
Robert F. Gessner *Valencia Community College*
Darryl V. Grennell *Alcorn State University*
Janice L. Horton *Missouri State University*
Chike A. Igboechi *Medgar Evers College, CUNY*
Stanley Kikkert *Mesa Community College*
Kevin B. Kiser *Cape Fear Community College*
Emily L. Lilly *University of Massachusetts Dartmouth*
Donald G. Lindmark *Cleveland State University*
Sue A. Looney *University of Alaska Anchorage*
Mary V. Mawn *Hudson Valley Community College*
Yilei Qian *Indiana University South Bend*
Laura B. Regassa *Georgia Southern University*
Timberley Roane *University of Colorado at Denver and Health Sciences Center*
Pushpa Samkutty *Southern University*
Lisa M. Schechter *University of Missouri-St. Louis*
Lois V. Sealy *Valencia Community College*
Susan Skelly *Rutgers University*
John G. Steiert *Missouri State University*
Jolie A. Stepaniak *Henry Ford Community College*
Gregory Weigel *University of Central Florida*
Roseann S. White *University of Central Florida*
John M. Zamora *Middle Tennessee State University*

I would like to thank all the people at McGraw-Hill for their efforts and support. It is always a pleasure to work with such a professional and competent group of people. Special thanks go to Michelle Watnick, Publisher;   Jim Connely Sr., Sponsoring Editor; Darlene M. Schueller, Developmental Editor; Tami Petsche, Marketing Manager; Joyce Watters, Project Manager; Lori Hancock, Photo Research Coordinator; and Brenda Rolwes, Designer; and many others who worked "behind the scenes."

Microscopy

1

Although there are many kinds of microscopes available to the microbiologist today, only four types will be described here for our use: the brightfield, darkfield, phase-contrast, and fluorescence microscopes. If you have had extensive exposure to microscopy in previous courses, this unit may not be of great value to you; however, if the study of microorganisms is a new field of study for you, there is a great deal of information that you need to acquire about the proper use of these instruments.

Microscopes in a college laboratory represent a considerable investment and require special care to prevent damage to the lenses and mechanical parts. A microscope may be used by several people during the day and moved from the work area to storage; which results in a much greater chance for damage to the instrument than if the microscope were used by only a single person.

The complexity of some of the more expensive microscopes also requires that certain adjustments be made periodically. Knowing how to make these adjustments to get the equipment to perform properly is very important. An attempt is made in the five exercises of this unit to provide the necessary assistance for getting the most out of the equipment.

Microscopy should be as fascinating to the beginner as it is to the professional of long standing; however, only with intelligent understanding can the beginner approach the achievement that occurs with years of experience.

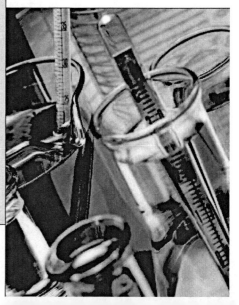

Brightfield Microscopy

1

e x e r c i s e

A microscope that allows light rays to pass directly to the eye without being deflected by an intervening opaque plate in the condenser is called a *brightfield microscope.* This is the conventional type of instrument encountered by students in beginning courses in biology; it is also the first type to be used in this laboratory.

All brightfield microscopes have certain things in common, yet they differ somewhat in mechanical operation. Similarities and differences of various makes are discussed in this exercise so that you will know how to use the instrument that is available to you. Before attending the first laboratory session in which the microscope is used, read over this exercise and answer all the questions on the Laboratory Report. Your instructor may require that the Laboratory Report be handed in prior to doing any laboratory work.

Care of the Instrument

Microscopes represent considerable investment and can be damaged easily if certain precautions are not observed. The following suggestions cover most hazards.

Transport When carrying your microscope from one part of the room to another, use both hands to hold the instrument, as illustrated in figure 1.1. If it is carried with only one hand and allowed to dangle at your side, there is always the danger of collision with furniture or some other object. And, *under no circumstances should one attempt to carry two microscopes at one time.*

Clutter Keep your workstation uncluttered while doing microscopy. Keep unnecessary books and other materials away from your work area. A clear work area promotes efficiency and results in fewer accidents.

Electric Cord Microscopes have been known to tumble off of tabletops when students have entangled a foot in a dangling electric cord. Don't let the electric cord on your microscope dangle in such a way as to risk foot entanglement.

Lens Care At the beginning of each laboratory period, check the lenses to make sure they are clean. At the end of each lab session, be sure to wipe any immersion

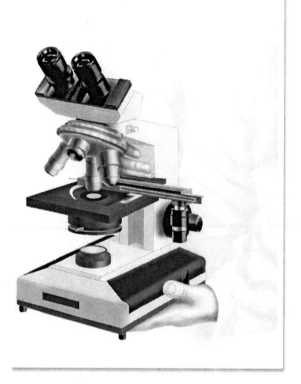

Figure 1.1 The microscope should be held firmly with both hands while being carried.

oil off the immersion lens if it has been used. More specifics about lens care are provided on page 6.

Dust Protection In most laboratories dustcovers are used to protect the instruments during storage. If one is available, place it over the microscope at the end of the period.

Components

Before we discuss the procedures for using a microscope, let's identify the principal parts of the instrument as illustrated in figure 1.2.

Framework All microscopes have a basic frame structure, which includes the **arm** and **base.** To this framework all other parts are attached. On many of

Microbiology, 11th Edition, Short Version

EXERCISE 1 ❚ Brightfield Microscopy

Figure 1.2 The compound microscope.
(Courtesy of the Olympus Corporation, Lake Success, NY)

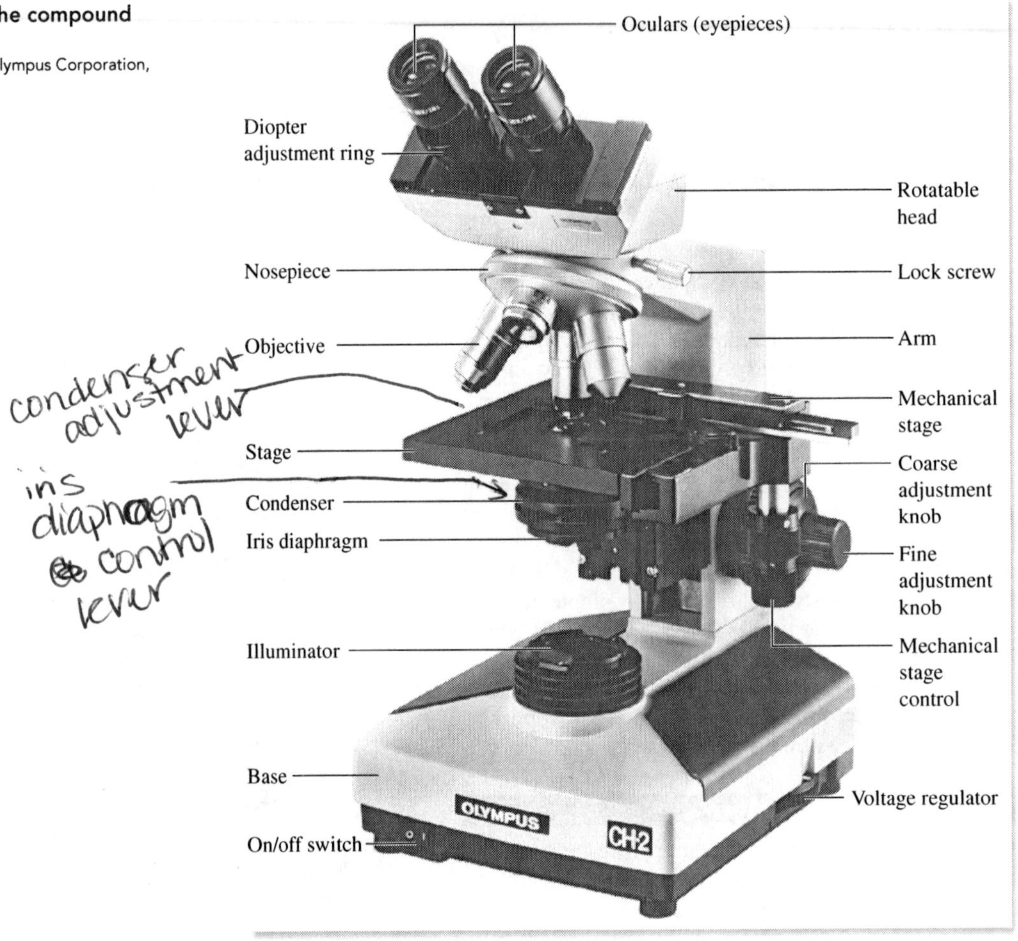

Oculars (eyepieces)

Diopter adjustment ring

Rotatable head

Nosepiece

Lock screw

Objective

Arm

Mechanical stage

Stage

Coarse adjustment knob

Condenser

Iris diaphragm

Fine adjustment knob

Illuminator

Mechanical stage control

Base

Voltage regulator

On/off switch

condenser adjustment lever

iris diaphragm & control lever

the older microscopes the base is not rigidly attached to the arm as is the case in figure 1.2; instead, a pivot point is present that enables one to tilt the arm backward to adjust the eyepoint height.

Stage The horizontal platform that supports the microscope slide is called the **stage.** Note that it has a clamping device, the **mechanical stage,** which is used for holding and moving the slide around on the stage. Note, also, the location of the **mechanical stage control** in figure 1.2.

Light Source In the base of most microscopes is positioned some kind of light source. Ideally, the lamp should have a **voltage control** to vary the intensity of light. The microscope in figure 1.2 has a knurled wheel on the right side of its base to regulate the voltage supplied to the light bulb.

Most microscopes have some provision for reducing light intensity with a **neutral density filter.** Such

a filter is often needed to reduce the intensity of light below the lower limit allowed by the voltage control. On microscopes such as the Olympus CH-2, one can simply place a neutral density filter over the light source in the base. On some microscopes a filter is built into the base.

Lens Systems All compound microscopes have three lens systems: the oculars, the objectives, and the condenser. Figure 1.3 illustrates the light path through these three systems.

The **ocular,** or eyepiece, is a complex piece, located at the top of the instrument, that consists of two or more internal lenses and usually has a magnification of 10×. Most modern microscopes (figure 1.2) have two ocular (binocular) lenses.

Three or more **objectives** are usually present. Note that they are attached to a rotatable **nosepiece,** which makes it possible to move them into position over a slide. Objectives on most laboratory micro-

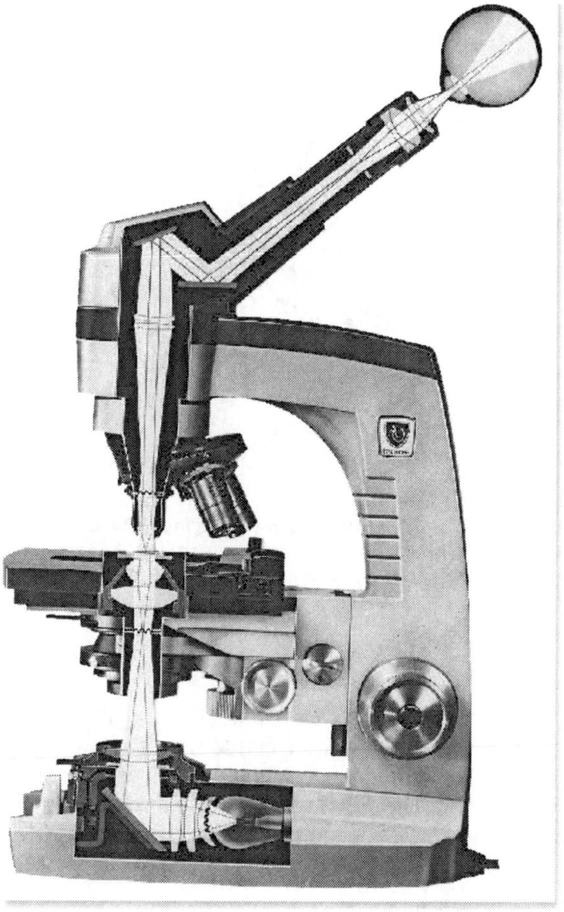

Figure 1.3 The light pathway of a microscope.

scopes have magnifications of 10×, 40×, and 100×, designated as **low power, high-dry,** and **oil immersion,** respectively. Some microscopes will have a fourth objective for rapid scanning of microscopic fields that is only 4×.

The total magnification of a compound microscope is determined by multiplying the power of the ocular lens times the power of the objective lens used. Thus, the magnification of a microscope in which the oil immersion lens is being used is:

$$10 \times 100 = 1000$$

The third lens system is the **condenser,** which is located under the stage. It collects and directs the light from the lamp to the slide being studied. Unlike the ocular and objective lenses, the condenser lens does not affect the magnifying power of the compound microscope. The condenser can be moved up and down by a knob under the stage. A **diaphragm** within the condenser regulates the amount of light that reaches the slide. Microscopes that lack a voltage control on the light source rely entirely on the diaphragm for con-

trolling light intensity. On the Olympus microscope in figure 1.2, the diaphragm is controlled by turning a knurled ring. On some microscopes, a diaphragm lever is present. Figure 1.3 illustrates the location of the condenser and diaphragm.

Focusing Knobs The concentrically arranged **coarse adjustment** and **fine adjustment knobs** on the side of the microscope are used for bringing objects into focus when studying an object on a slide. On some microscopes, these knobs are not positioned concentrically as shown here.

Ocular Adjustments On binocular microscopes, one must be able to change the distance between the oculars and to make diopter changes for eye differences. On most microscopes, the interocular distance is changed by simply pulling apart or pushing together the oculars.

To make diopter adjustments, one focuses first with the right eye only. Without touching the focusing knobs, diopter adjustments are then made on the left eye by turning the knurled **diopter adjustment ring** (figure 1.2) on the left ocular until a sharp image is seen. One should now be able to see sharp images with both eyes.

Resolution

It would appear that the magnification of a microscope is only limited by the magnifying power of a lens system. However, in reality the limit for most light microscopes is 1000× which is set by an intrinsic property of lenses called **resolving power.** The resolving power of a lens is its ability to completely separate two objects in a microscopic field. The resolving power is given by the formula $d = 0.5\ \lambda/NA$. The limit of resolution, d, or the distance between the two objects, is a function of two properties: the wavelength of the light used to observe a specimen, λ, and a property of lenses called the **numerical aperture** or NA. Numerical aperture is a mathematical expression that describes how the condenser lens concentrates and focuses the light rays from the light source. Its value is maximized when the light rays are focused into a cone of light that then passes through the specimen into the objective lens. However, because some light is refracted or bent as it passes from glass into air, the refracted light rays are lost, and as a result the numerical aperture is diminished (figure 1.4). The greater the loss of refracted light, the lower the numerical aperture. The final result is that the resolving power is greatly reduced.

For any light microscope, the limit of resolution is about 0.2 μm. This means that two objects closer than 0.2 μm would not be seen as two distinct objects.

**Microbiology, 11th Edition,
Short Version**

EXERCISE 1 ▌ Brightfield Microscopy

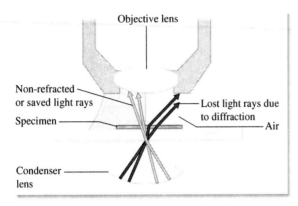

Figure 1.4 Immersion oil, having the same refractive index as glass, prevents light loss due to diffraction.

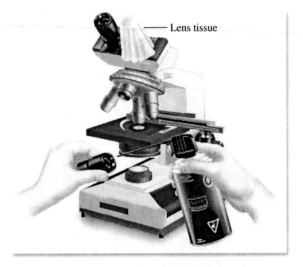

Figure 1.5 When oculars are removed for cleaning, cover the ocular opening with lens tissue. A blast from an air syringe or gas cannister removes dust and lint.

Because bacterial cells are about 1 μm, the cells can be resolved by the light microscope but that is not the case for internal structures in bacterial cells that are smaller than 0.2 μm.

In order to maximize the resolving power from a lens system, the following should be considered:

- A **blue filter** should be placed over the light source because the shorter wave length of the resulting light will provide maximum resolution.
- The condenser should be kept at the highest position that allows the maximum amount of light to enter the objective lens and therefore limit the amount of light lost due to refraction.
- The diaphragm should not be stopped down too much. While closing the diaphragm improves the contrast, it also reduces the numerical aperture.
- **Immersion oil** should be used between the slide and the 100× objective lens. This is a special oil that has the same refractive index as glass. When placed between the specimen and objective lens, the oil forms a continuous lens system that limits the loss of light due to refraction.

The bottom line is that for magnification to increase, resolution must also increase. Thus, a greater magnification cannot simply be achieved by adding a 20× ocular lens.

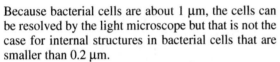
Lens Care

Keeping the lenses of your microscope clean is a constant concern. Unless all lenses are kept free of dust, oil, and other contaminants, they are unable to achieve the degree of resolution that is intended. Consider the following suggestions for cleaning the various lens components:

Cleaning Tissues Only lint-free, optically safe tissues should be used to clean lenses. Tissues free of abrasive grit fall in this category. Booklets of lens tissue are most widely used for this purpose. Although several types of boxed tissues are also safe, *use only the type of tissue that is recommended by your instructor* (figure 1.5).

Solvents Various liquids can be used for cleaning microscope lenses. Green soap with warm water works very well. Xylene is universally acceptable. Alcohol and acetone are also recommended, but often with some reservations. Acetone is a powerful solvent that could possibly dissolve the lens mounting cement in some objective lenses if it were used too liberally. When it is used it should be used sparingly. Your instructor will inform you as to what solvents can be used on the lenses of your microscope.

Oculars The best way to determine if your eyepiece is clean is to rotate it between the thumb and forefinger as you look through the microscope. A rotating pattern will be evidence of dirt.

If cleaning the top lens of the ocular with lens tissue fails to remove the debris, one should try cleaning the lower lens with lens tissue and blowing off any excess lint with an air syringe or gas cannister. *Whenever the ocular is removed from the microscope, it is imperative that a piece of lens tissue be placed over the open end of the microscope as illustrated in figure 1.5.*

Brightfield Microscopy ▌ EXERCISE 1

Objectives Objective lenses often become soiled by materials from slides or fingers. A piece of lens tissue moistened with green soap and water, or one of the acceptable solvents mentioned on page 6, will usually remove whatever is on the lens. Sometimes a cotton swab with a solvent will work better than lens tissue. At any time that the image on the slide is unclear or cloudy, assume at once that the objective you are using is soiled.

Condenser Dust often accumulates on the top surface of the condenser; thus, wiping it off occasionally with lens tissue is desirable.

Procedures

If your microscope has three objectives, you have three magnification options: (1) low-power, or 100× total magnification, (2) high-dry magnification, which is 400× total with a 40× objective, and (3) 1000× total magnification with a 100× oil immersion objective.

Whether you use the low-power objective or the oil immersion objective will depend on how much magnification is necessary. Generally speaking, however, it is best to start with the low-power objective and progress to the higher magnifications as your study progresses. Consider the following suggestions for setting up your microscope and making microscopic observations.

Low-Power Examination The main reason for starting with the low-power objective is to enable you to explore the slide to look for the object you are planning to study. Once you have found what you are looking for, you can proceed to higher magnifications. Use the following steps when exploring a slide with the low-power objective:

1. Position the slide on the stage with the material to be studied on the *upper* surface of the slide. Figure 1.6 illustrates how the slide must be held in place by the mechanical stage retainer lever.
2. Turn on the light source, using a *minimum* amount of voltage. If necessary, reposition the slide so that the stained material on the slide is in the *exact center* of the light source.
3. Check the condenser to see that it has been raised to its highest point.
4. If the low-power objective is not directly over the center of the stage, rotate it into position. Be sure that as you rotate the objective into position it clicks into its locked position.
5. Turn the coarse adjustment knob to lower the objective until it stops. A built-in stop will prevent the objective from touching the slide.

6. While looking down through the ocular (or oculars), bring the object into focus by turning the fine adjustment focusing knob. Don't readjust the coarse adjustment knob. If you are using a binocular microscope, it will also be necessary to adjust the interocular distance and diopter adjustment to match your eyes.
7. Manipulate the diaphragm lever to reduce or increase the light intensity to produce the clearest, sharpest image. Note that as you close down the diaphragm to reduce the light intensity, the contrast improves and the depth of field increases. Stopping down the diaphragm when using the low-power objective does not decrease resolution.
8. Once an image is visible, move the slide about to search out what you are looking for. The slide is moved by turning the knobs that move the mechanical stage.
9. Check the cleanliness of the ocular, using the procedure outlined earlier.
10. Once you have identified the structures to be studied and wish to increase the magnification, you may proceed to either high-dry or oil immersion magnification. However, before changing objectives, *be sure to center the object you wish to observe.*

High-Dry Examination To proceed from low-power to high-dry magnification, all that is necessary is to rotate the high-dry objective into position and open up the diaphragm somewhat. It may be necessary to make a minor adjustment with the fine adjustment knob to sharpen up the image, but *the coarse ad-justment knob should not be touched.*

Good quality modern microscopes are **parfocal.** This means that the image will remain in focus when changing from a lower-power objective lens to a higher-power lens. Only minimal focusing should be necessary with the fine focus adjustment.

When increasing the lighting, be sure to open up the diaphragm first instead of increasing the voltage on your lamp; the reason is that *lamp life is greatly extended when used at low voltage.* If the field is not

Figure 1.6 The slide must be properly positioned as the retainer lever is moved to the right.

Microbiology, 11th Edition,
Short Version

EXERCISE 1 ▌ Brightfield Microscopy

Table 1.1 Relationship of Working Distance to Magnification

LENS	MAGNIFICATION	FOCAL LENGTH (mm)	WORKING DISTANCE (mm)
Low-power	10×	16.0	7.7
High-dry	40×	4.0	0.3
Oil immersion	100×	1.8	0.12

bright enough after opening the diaphragm, feel free to increase the voltage. A final point: Keep the condenser at its highest point.

Oil Immersion Techniques The oil immersion lens derives its name from the fact that a special mineral oil is interposed between the specimen and the 100× objective lens. As stated previously, this reduces light diffraction and maximizes the numerical aperture to improve the resolution. The use of oil in this way enhances the resolving power of the microscope. Figure 1.4 reveals this phenomenon.

With parfocal objectives one can go directly to oil immersion from either low-power or high-dry. On some microscopes, however, going from low-power to high-power and then to oil immersion is better. Once the microscope has been brought into focus at one magnification, the oil immersion lens can be rotated into position without fear of striking the slide.

Before rotating the oil immersion lens into position, however, a drop of immersion oil must be placed on the slide. An oil immersion lens should never be used without oil. Incidentally, if the oil appears cloudy, it should be discarded.

When using the oil immersion lens, it is best to open the diaphragm as much as possible. Stopping down the diaphragm tends to limit the resolving power of the optics. In addition, the condenser must be kept at its highest point. If different colored filters are available for the lamp housing, it is best to use blue or greenish filters to enhance the resolving power.

Since the oil immersion lens will be used extensively in all bacteriological studies, it is of paramount importance that you learn how to use this lens properly. Using this lens takes a little practice due to the difficulties usually encountered in manipulating the lighting. It is important for all beginning students

to appreciate that the working distance of a lens, the distance between the lens and microscope slide, decreases significantly as the magnification of the lens increases (table 1.1). Hence, the potential for damage to the oil immersion lens because of a collision with the microscope slide is very great. A final comment of importance: At the end of the laboratory period remove all immersion oil from the lens tip with lens tissue.

Putting It Away

When you take a microscope from the cabinet at the beginning of the period, you expect it to be clean and in proper working condition. The next person to use the instrument after you have used it will expect the same consideration. A few moments of care at the end of the period will ensure these conditions. Check over the following list of items at the end of each period before you return the microscope to the cabinet.

1. Remove the slide from the stage.
2. If immersion oil has been used, wipe it off the lens and stage with lens tissue. (Do not wipe oil off slides you wish to keep. Simply put them into a slide box and let the oil drain off.)
3. Rotate the low-power objective into position.
4. If the microscope has been inclined, return it to an erect position.
5. If the microscope has a built-in movable lamp, raise the lamp to its highest position.
6. If the microscope has a long attached electric cord, wrap it around the base.
7. Adjust the mechanical stage so that it does not project too far on either side.
8. Replace the dustcover.
9. If the microscope has a separate transformer, return it to its designated place.
10. Return the microscope to its correct place in the cabinet.

Laboratory Report

Before the microscope is to be used in the laboratory, answer all the questions on Laboratory Report 1 that pertain to brightfield microscopy. Preparation on your part prior to going to the laboratory will greatly facilitate your understanding. Your instructor may wish to collect this report at the *beginning of the period* on the first day that the microscope is to be used in class.

Microbiology, 11th Edition,
Short Version

Brightfield Microscopy (continued)

4. The total magnification achieved when using a 100× oil immersion lens with 10× binocular eyepieces is
   a. 10×.
   b. 100×.
   c. 200×.
   d. 1000×.
   e. 2000×.

5. The most useful adjustment for increasing image contrast in low-power magnification is
   a. closing down the diaphragm.
   b. closing one eye.
   c. opening up the diaphragm.
   d. placing a drop of oil on the slide.
   e. using a blue filter.

6. Before the oil immersion lens is rotated into place, you should
   a. center the object of interest in the preceding lens.
   b. lower the stage with use of the coarse focus adjustment knob.
   c. place a drop of oil on the slide.
   d. Both (a) and (c) are correct.
   e. All are correct.

4. _____

5. _____

6. _____

Survey of Microorganisms

PART 2

Microorganisms abound in the environment. Eukaryotic microbes such as protozoa, algae, diatoms, and amoebas are plentiful in ponds and lakes. Bacteria are found associated with animals, occur abundantly in the soil and in water systems, and have even been isolated from core samples taken from deep within the earth's crust. Bacteria are also present in the air where they are distributed by convection currents that transport them from other environments. The Archaea, modern day relatives of early microorganisms, occupy some of the most extreme environments such as acidic-volcanic hot springs, anaerobic environments devoid of any oxygen, and lakes and salt marshes excessively high in sodium chloride. Cyanobacteria are photosynthetic prokaryotes that can be found growing in ponds and lakes, on limestone rocks, and even on the shingles that protect the roofs of our homes. Fungi are a very diverse group of microorganisms that are found in most common environments. For example, they degrade complex molecules in the soil, thus contributing to its fertility. Sometimes, however, they can be nuisance organisms; they form mildew in our bathroom showers and their spores cause allergies. The best way of describing the distribution of microorganisms is to say that they are ubiquitous, or found everywhere.

Intriguing questions to biologists are how are the various organisms related to one another and where do the individual organisms fit in an evolutionary scheme? Molecular biology techniques have provided a means to analyze the genetic relatedness of the organisms that comprise the biological world and determine where the various organisms fit into an evolutionary scheme. By comparing the sequence of ribosomal RNA molecules, coupled with biochemical data, investigators have developed a phylogenetic tree that illustrates the current thinking on the placement of the various organisms into such

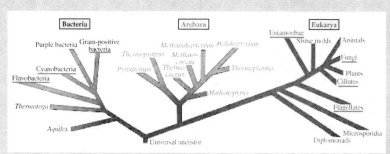

© Roberto Osti Illustrations. Used by permission.

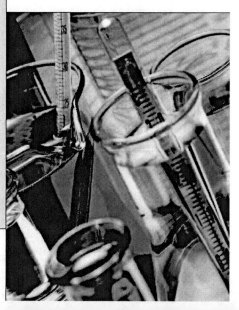

a scheme. This evolutionary scheme divides the biological world into three domains.

Domain Bacteria These organisms have a prokaryotic cell structure. They lack organelles such as mitochondria and chloroplasts, are devoid of an organized nucleus with a nuclear membrane, and possess 70S ribosomes that are inhibited by many broad-spectrum antibiotics. The vast majority of organisms are enclosed in a cell wall composed of peptidoglycan. The bacteria and cyanobacteria are members of this domain.

Domain Eukarya Organisms in this domain have a eukaryotic cell structure. They contain membrane-bound organelles such as mitochondria and chloroplasts, an organized nucleus enclosed in a nuclear membrane, and 80S ribosomes that are not inhibited by broad spectrum antibiotics. Plants, animals, and microorganisms such as protozoa, algae, and fungi belong in this domain. Plants have cell walls composed of cellulose and fungi have cell walls composed of chitin. In contrast, animal cells lack a cell wall structure.

Domain Archaea The Archaea exhibit the characteristics of both the bacteria and Eukarya. These organisms are considered to be the relatives of ancient microbes that existed during Archean times. Like their bacterial counterparts, they possess a simple cell structure that lacks organelles and an organized nucleus. They have 70S ribosomes like bacteria but the protein makeup and morphology of their ribosomes are more similar to eukaryotic ribosomes. Like eukaryotes, the ribosomes in Archaea are not sensitive to antibiotics. They have a cell wall but its structure is not composed of peptidoglycan. The principal habitats of these organisms are extreme environments such as volcanic hot springs, environments with excessively high salt, and environments devoid of oxygen. Thus, they are referred to as "extremophiles." The acido-thermophiles, the halobacteria, and the methanogens (methane bacteria) are examples of the Archaea.

In the exercises of Part 2, you will have the opportunity to study some of these organisms. In pond water, you may see amoebas, protozoans, various algae, diatoms, and cyanobacteria. You will sample for the presence of bacteria by exposing growth media to various environments. The fungi will be studied by looking at cultures and preparing slides of these organisms. Because the Archaea occur in extreme conditions and also require specialized culture techniques, it is unlikely that you will encounter any of these organisms.

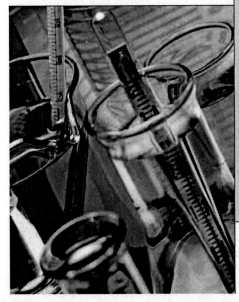

32

Protozoa, Algae, and Cyanobacteria

In this exercise, a study will be made of protists and cyanobacteria that live in pond water. Containers of water and bottom debris from various ponds will be available for study. Illustrations and text provided in this exercise will be used to assist you in your attempt to identify the various organisms. Organisms that are bluish-green will probably be cyanobacteria (once categorized as blue-green algae). Most others will be protists. However, small nematodes, insect larvae, microcrustaceans, rotifers, and other invertebrates could be present. Supplementary books on the laboratory bookshelf may also be available to help you with identification of the organisms that are not described or diagrammed in the short text of this exercise.

The purpose of this exercise is to provide an opportunity for you to become familiar with common pond-dwelling microorganisms and to appreciate the vast diversity that exists in a drop of pond water. You will also become familiar with the differences among several groups by comparing their major characteristics. The extent to which you will be held accountable for the names of various organisms will be determined by your instructor. The amount of time available for this laboratory exercise will determine the depth and scope to be pursued.

To study the microorganisms of pond water, it will be necessary to make wet mount slides. The procedure for making such slides is very simple. All that is necessary is to place a drop of suspended organisms on a microscope slide and cover it with a cover glass. If several different samples are available, you should record the number of the container (from which you took your sample) on your slide with a marking pen. As you prepare your slides, observe the following guidelines below.

Materials

* bottles of pond-water samples
* microscope slides and cover glasses
* rubber-bulbed pipettes and forceps
* marking pen
* reference books

1. Clean a slide and cover glass with soap and water, rinse thoroughly, and dry. Do not attempt to study a slide that lacks a cover glass.

2. When using a pipette, insert it into the bottom of the sample bottle to get a maximum number of organisms. Very few organisms will be found swimming around in middepth of the bottle.
3. To remove filamentous algae from a sample bottle, use forceps. Avoid putting too much material on the slides.
4. Explore the slide first with the low-power objective. Reduce the lighting with the iris diaphragm; this is very important. Keep the condenser at its highest point.
5. When you find an organism of interest, swing the high-dry objective into position and adjust the lighting to get optimum contrast. If your microscope has phase-contrast elements, use them.
6. Refer to figures 5.1 through 5.6 and the text on these pages to identify the various organisms that you encounter.
7. Record your observations on the Laboratory Report.

Survey of Organisms

An impressive variety of protists and cyanobacteria will likely be encountered during this laboratory exercise. You will be asked to identify and categorize these organisms based on their morphological characteristics. Traditionally, such morphological characteristics were used to construct formal classification schemes; however, genetic analyses have demonstrated that such classification schemes do not necessarily represent evolutionary relationships between organisms. Presently, there is a lively debate among protistologists as to which taxonomic scheme (and there are many) of protists should be accepted worldwide. Because of this lack of consensus among scientists about how to classify protists, and because true evolutionary relationships cannot be determined simply by observing organisms, you will use an informal system based on morphology to categorize the organisms that you encounter in this exercise. The following table will help you understand some of the major morphological groups of the organisms that you may see. **Please keep in mind that these are not formally recognized taxonomic groups,** but are useful for identifying and categorizing organisms in the laboratory based on specific physical traits.

Microbiology, 11th Edition,
Short Version

EXERCISE 5 ▌ Protozoa, Algae, and Cyanobacteria

Table 5.1   Classification of Organisms

PROKARYOTES (DOMAIN PROKARYA)	EUKARYOTES (DOMAIN EUKARYA)

Cyanobacteria (Figure 5.6)	Protists:
	  Protozoa:
	    Flagellates (figure 5.1, illustrations 1–4)
	    Amoebae (figure 5.1, illustrations 5–8)
	    Ciliates (figure 5.1, illustrations 9–24)
	  Algae:
	    Euglenoids (euglenozoa) (figure 5.2, illustrations 1–6)
	    Green algae (chlorophytes) (figure 5.2, illustrations 8, 14, 15, 19, 20; figure 5.3; figure 5.4)
	    Golden-brown algae (chrysophytes) (figure 5.2, illustration 16)
	    Synurales (figure 5.2, illustration 13)
	    Yellow-green algae (xanthophytes) (figure 5.3, illustrations 5, 6)
	    Diatoms (bacillariophytes) (figure 5.5)
	    Dinoflagellates (figure 5.2, illustrations 17, 18)

Eukaryotes

The Protists

The protists are a large, paraphyletic group of organisms. Generally, protists are eukaryotic organisms that cannot be classified as plants, fungi, or animals. The majority of protists are unicellular, although some are colonial and some are multicellular. None have differentiated tissues.

Protozoa

Generally, moving, nonpigmented, single-celled organisms are referred to as "protozoa." Protozoa include heterotrophic flagellates, amoebae, ciliates, and apicomplexans. Either the entire cell will move, or the cell will be attached to a substrate and only parts of the cell will move. With respect to movement, there are three major means of locomotion of free-living protozoa; pseudopodia (found in amoeboid cells), flagella (found in flagellates), cilia (found in ciliates), and gliding (diatoms). These eukaryotic cells are bound by a plasma membrane that may have additional surface modifications depending on the species. All have a distinct nucleus, ribosomes, and mitochondria. Some possess a cytostome (for ingestion of food) and one or more contractile vacuoles (for osmoregulation). All can reproduce asexually, and some species can also reproduce sexually.

1. Flagellates

Flagellates contain one or several flagella, which are long whip-like structures that, internally, have a 9 + 2 arrangement of microtubules. During asexual reproduction, most flagellates divide longitudinally. Flagellated cells can be colorless and, thus, are heterotrophic (e.g., *Heteronema*) or pigmented (shades of green or golden brown). Pigmented, flagellated cells will be dis-cussed later. Illustrations 1 through 4 in figure 5.1 show colorless flagellates.

2. Amoeboid Cells

These organisms are sometimes simply called "amoeba." Most move by formation and extension of transitory pseudopodia, which are cytoplasmic extensions. Movement is generally slow. Amoebae are predators and usually feed on bacteria and protists by engulfing them and forming a food vacuole around the prey. Some amoebae that you might see today have a "test," a hard outer covering (e.g., *Arcella, Difflugia*). Illustrations 5 through 8 in figure 5.1 depict amoebae.

3. Ciliates

Ciliates are complex cells that possess two type of nuclei—a diploid micronucleus and a larger polyploid macronucleus. Ciliates are usually covered with many cilia, which are short, hairlike projections that beat in coordinated fashion to propel the cell forwards or backwards. Other than length, cilia are structurally very similar to flagella and have a 9 + 2 arrangement of internal microtubules; both cilia and flagella are covered by the plasma membrane. Some species are attached to a substrate (e.g., *Vorticella, Zoothamnium*) and use cilia to create feeding currents around the cytostome (mouth). The cytostome can be quite large for ingestion of food, which is usually bacteria or small protozoa. Ciliates can be colorless (e.g., *Stylonychia*), blue (*Stentor*), pink (*Blepharisma*), or green (*Paramecium bursaria*). The green color is due to the presence of endosymbiotic algal cells. Illustrations 9 through 24 in figure 5.1 depict representative ciliates.

4. Apicomplexa

Nearly all species in this group are parasitic. Most motile forms move by gliding. The genus *Plas-*

**Microbiology, 11th Edition,
Short Version**

Protozoa, Algae, and Cyanobacteria   ▮   EXERCISE 5

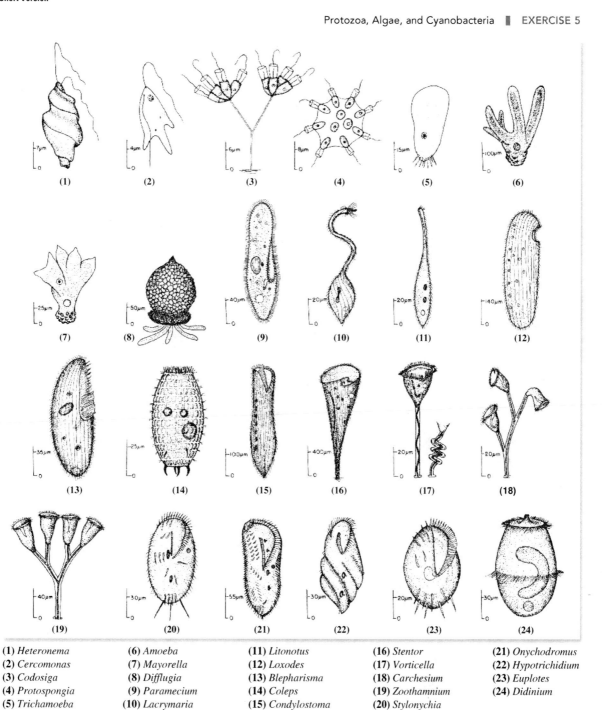

(1) Heteronema	(6) Amoeba	(11) Litonotus	(16) Stentor	(21) Onychodromus
(2) Cercomonas	(7) Mayorella	(12) Loxodes	(17) Vorticella	(22) Hypotrichidium
(3) Codosiga	(8) Difflugia	(13) Blepharisma	(18) Carchesium	(23) Euplotes
(4) Protospongia	(9) Paramecium	(14) Coleps	(19) Zoothamnium	(24) Didinium
(5) Trichamoeba	(10) Lacrymaria	(15) Condylostoma	(20) Stylonychia	

Figure 5.1   Protozoans.

modium is an extremely important member of this group because several of its species are the causative agents of malaria in humans. Malaria is responsible for more deaths of humans per year than any other disease caused by a eukaryotic parasite. You will not see apicomplexans today. Parasitic, unicellular, eukaryotic cells will not be discussed further in this exercise but realize that they represent thousands of species.

The Algae—Photosynthetic Protists

The majority of eukaryotic algae are placed in the subgroups (a) Chlorophyta/Chloroplastida if they

Microbiology, 11th Edition,
Short Version

EXERCISE 5 ▌ Protozoa, Algae, and Cyanobacteria

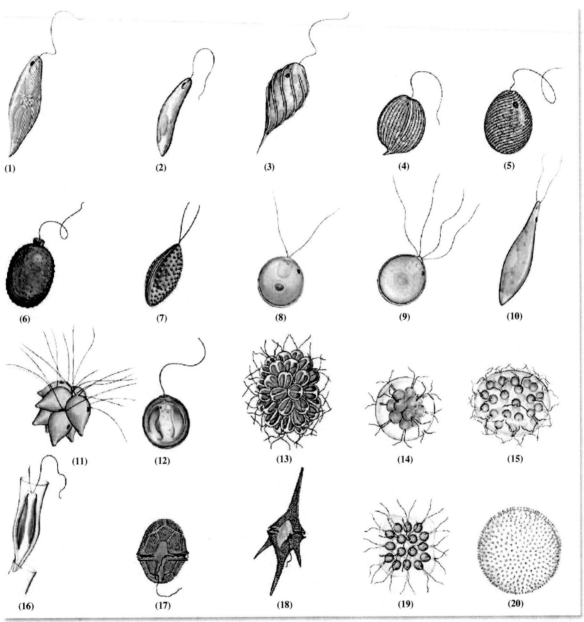

(1) *Euglena* (700X)
(2) *Euglena* (700X)
(3) *Phacus* (1000X)
(4) *Phacus* (350X)
(5) *Lepocinclis* (350X)

(6) *Trachelomonas* (1000X)
(7) *Phacotus* (1500X)
(8) *Chlamydomonas* (1000X)
(9) *Carteria* (1500X)
(10) *Chlorogonium* (1000X)

(11) *Pyrobotrys* (1000X)
(12) *Chrysococcus* (3000X)
(13) *Synura* (350X)
(14) *Pandorina* (350X)
(15) *Eudorina* (175X)

(16) *Dinobryon* (1000X)
(17) *Peridinium* (350X)
(18) *Ceratium* (175X)
(19) *Gonium* (350X)
(20) *Volvox* (100X)

Figure 5.2 Flagellated algae.
(Courtesy of the U.S. Environmental Protection Agency, Office of Research & Development, Cincinnati, OH 45268)

are green; (b) Rhodophyceae if they are red (both of these groups are within the cluster Archaeplastida); (c) Euglenozoa if they are euglenoid (within the cluster Excavata); (d) Alveolata if they are dino-flagellates (within the cluster Chromalveolata); or (e) Straemenopile if they are brown, golden-brown, or a diatom (within the cluster Chromalveolata). Algae can be unicelluar (see top two rows of figure 5.2), colonial (see the four illustrations in the lower-right corner of figure 5.2), or filamentous

Microbiology, 11th Edition,
Short Version

Protozoa, Algae, and Cyanobacteria ▌ EXERCISE 5

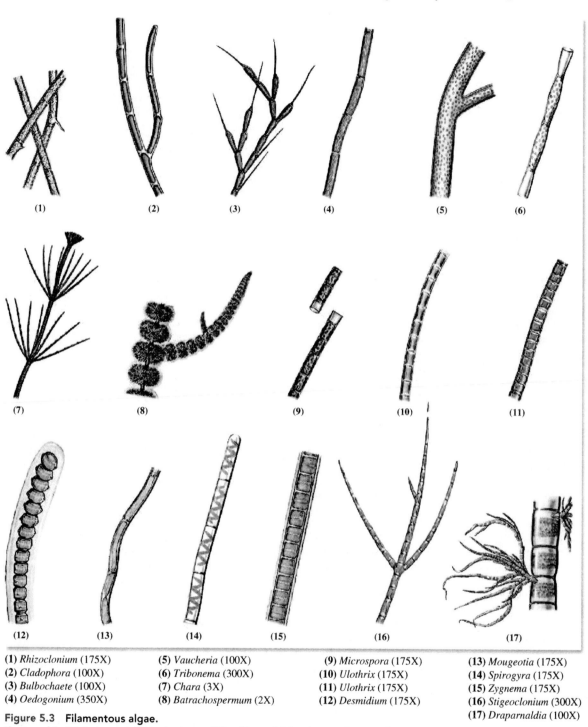

(1) *Rhizoclonium* (175X)	(5) *Vaucheria* (100X)	(9) *Microspora* (175X)	(13) *Mougeotia* (175X)
(2) *Cladophora* (100X)	(6) *Tribonema* (300X)	(10) *Ulothrix* (175X)	(14) *Spirogyra* (175X)
(3) *Bulbochaete* (100X)	(7) *Chara* (3X)	(11) *Ulothrix* (175X)	(15) *Zygnema* (175X)
(4) *Oedogonium* (350X)	(8) *Batrachospermum* (2X)	(12) *Desmidium* (175X)	(16) *Stigeoclonium* (300X)
			(17) *Draparnaldia* (100X)

Figure 5.3 Filamentous algae.
(Courtesy of the U.S. Environmental Protection Agency, Office of Research & Development, Cincinnati, OH 45268)

(figure 5.3). The undifferentiated algal structure is often referred to as a "thallus." It lacks the stem, root, and leaf structures that result from tissue specialization. These organisms are universally present where ample moisture, favorable temperature, and suffi- cient sunlight exist. Although a great many of them live submerged in water, some grow on soil or the surface of snow. Others grow on the bark of trees or the surface of rocks. Algae have distinct, visible nu- clei and chloroplasts. Chloroplasts are organelles that

**Microbiology, 11th Edition,
Short Version**

EXERCISE 5 ▮ Protozoa, Algae, and Cyanobacteria

contain thylakoids (parallel arrays of membranes), chlorophyll a, and other pigments. The reactions of photosynthesis take place in these organelles. The size, shape, distribution, and number of chloroplasts vary considerably among species. In some instances, a single chloroplast may occupy most of the cell space (e.g., *Chlamydomonas*). Several groups of algae (e.g., red algae) are rarely encountered in freshwater ponds. Following are descriptions of some of the more familiar freshwater groups.

1. Euglenoids (Euglenozoa/Excavata)

Illustrations 1 through 6 in figure 5.2 show typical euglenoids and represent four genera within this group. These unicells are flagellated (usually two flagella) and have no cell wall. Some have the ability to ingest food and assimilate organic molecules. Photosynthetic species have a photosensitive, red eyespot and chloroplasts that contain chlorophylls a and b and have a secondary origin. Three outer membranes surround the chloroplast. The euglenoid pellicle is located beneath the cell membrane and is made of proteinaceous strips such that some cells are capable of active, eye-catching distortion known as "euglenoid movement." Eulgenoid flagellates store "paramylon," a polysaccharide storage molecule that is unique to them.

2. Green Algae (Chlorophyta/Chloroplastida/Archaeplastida)

The majority of algae in ponds belong to this group. They are grass-green in color and have chlorophylls a and b. They store starch as an energy reserve. The archetype of the group may be *Chlamydomonas* (illustration 8, figure 5.2), a small, green, flagellated unicell that has been extensively studied. Many colonial forms such as *Pandorina*, *Eudorina*, *Gonium*, and *Volvox* (illustrations 14, 15, 19, and 20 in figure 5.2) exist. Except for *Vaucheria* and *Tribonema* (Xanthophyceae) and *Batrachospermum* (illustration 8; Rhodophyceae) all of the filamentous forms illustrated in figure 5.3 belong to Chloroplastida. All of the nonfilamentous, nonflagellated algae shown in figure 5.4 also are green algae.

The "desmids" are a unique group of green algae (illustrations 12 in figure 5.3 and 16–20 in figure 5.4). With the exception of a few species, the cells of desmids consist of two similar halves, or semi-cells. The two halves are separated by a constriction, the isthmus.

3. Golden-Brown Algae (Chrysophyceae/Stramenopile/Chromalveolata)

This large diverse division contains more than 6000 species. These organisms store food in the form of oils and leucosin (chrysolaminarin), a storage poly-saccharide. Plastid pigments include chlorophylls a and c and fucoxanthin, a brownish pigment. It is the combination of fucoxanthin, other yellow pigments, and the chlorophylls that causes most of these algae to appear golden-brown. These are four outer membranes associated with the chloroplast. Representatives of this division, such as *Dinobryon*, are illustrated in figure 5.2 (illustration 16).

4. Synurales (Chromalveolata)

This small group contains a familiar genus, *Synura* (illustration 13 in figure 5.2). Members of this group contain chlorophylls a and c and several types of xanthin pigments. Silica scales cover the cells, most of which are flagellated.

5. Xanthophyceae (yellow-green algae; Chromalveolata)

Members of this group contain chlorophylls a and c and several types of xanthin pigments but not fucoxanthin. Genera that you might see today include *Tribonema* and *Vaucheria*, both of which are filamentous. These genera are diagrammed in illustrations 5 and 6 in figure 5.3.

6. Phaeophyceae (Stramenopile/Chromalveolata)

Members of this group are commonly called "brown algae." With the exception of three freshwater species, all members of this group live in saltwater environments; thus, it is unlikely that you will encounter brown algae during this lab exercise. These algae have essentially the same pigments seen in the golden-brown algae, but they appear brown because of the masking effect of the greater amount of fucoxanthin. The chloroplasts have four outer membranes. Food storage in the brown algae is in the form of laminarin, a polysaccharide, and mannitol, a sugar alcohol. All species of brown algae are multicellular and sessile. Most seaweeds (e.g., kelp) are brown algae.

7. Bacillariophyta (Stramenopile/Chromalveolata)

Members of this group include the diatoms (figure 5.5). The diatoms are unique in that they have hard cell walls made of tightly integrated silicified elements that are constructed in two halves, or "valves." The two valves fit together like a lid on a box. Skeletons of dead diatoms accumulate on the ocean bottom to form *diatomite*, or "diatomaceous earth," which is commercially available as an excellent polishing compound. It is postulated by some that much of our petroleum reserves may have been formulated by the accumulation of oil from dead diatoms over millions of years. Plastid pigments in diatoms are similar to those in brown

Protozoa, Algae, and Cyanobacteria ▮ EXERCISE 5

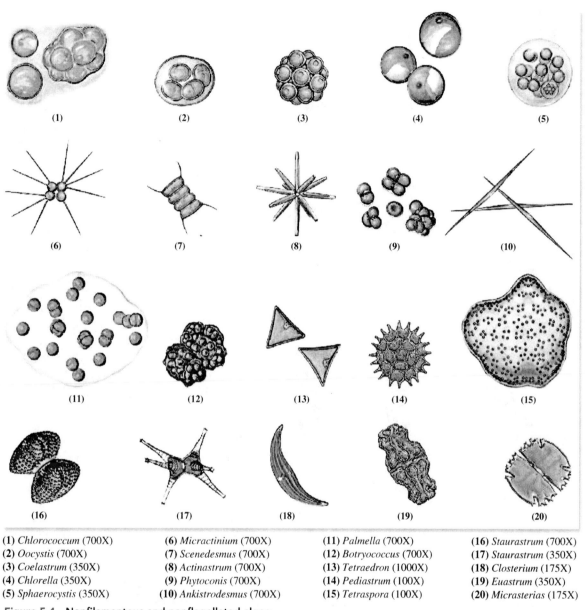

(1) *Chlorococcum* (700X)	(6) *Micractinium* (700X)	(11) *Palmella* (700X)	(16) *Staurastrum* (700X)
(2) *Oocystis* (700X)	(7) *Scenedesmus* (700X)	(12) *Botryococcus* (700X)	(17) *Staurastrum* (350X)
(3) *Coelastrum* (350X)	(8) *Actinastrum* (700X)	(13) *Tetraedron* (1000X)	(18) *Closterium* (175X)
(4) *Chlorella* (350X)	(9) *Phytoconis* (700X)	(14) *Pediastrum* (100X)	(19) *Euastrum* (350X)
(5) *Sphaerocystis* (350X)	(10) *Ankistrodesmus* (700X)	(15) *Tetraspora* (100X)	(20) *Micrasterias* (175X)

Figure 5.4 Nonfilamentous and nonflagellated algae.
(Courtesy of the U.S. Environmental Protection Agency, Office of Research & Development, Cincinnati, OH 45268)

algae (i.e., chlorophylls a and c, fucoxanthin). The chloroplasts have four outer membranes. Chrysolaminarin, a type of laminarin, and sometimes oil are the storage molecules.

8. Dinozoa (Alveolata/Chromalveolata)
Members of this group are commonly called "dinoflagellates" or "fire algae." These unicellular, flagellated protists live in both marine and freshwater environments. You could possibly see *Peridinium* and *Ceratium* or others during this exercise (figure 5.2, illustrations 17 and 18). Most

dinoflagellates have interlocking cellulose plates that form a theca. The thecal plates are within alveoil (membranous sacs) that are interior to the plasma membrane; therefore, these cellulose plates differ greatly from a plant's cell wall, which is exterior to the plasma membrane. Dinoflagellates have two flagella: a transverse flagellum sits in a groove and propels the cell and longitudinal flagellum appears to act as a steering device. Many species of marine dinoflagellates are bioluminescent and are easily seen at night in the wake of a moving boat. Some marine dinoflagellates are responsible

**Microbiology, 11th Edition,
Short Version**

EXERCISE 5 ▌ Protozoa, Algae, and Cyanobacteria

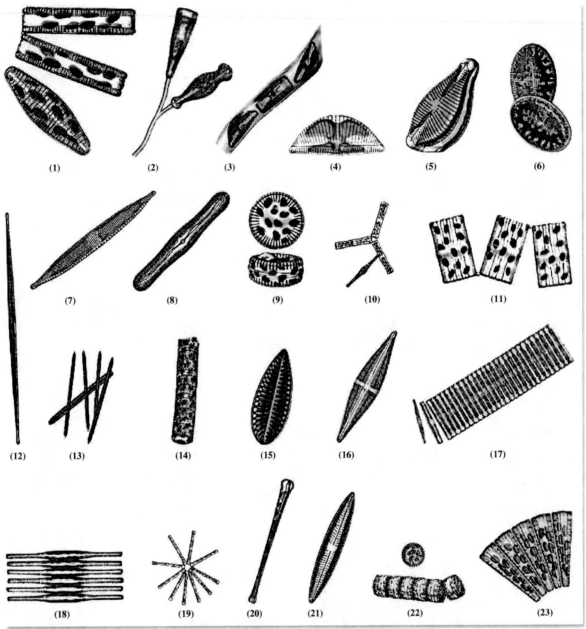

(1) *Diatoma* (1000X)
(2) *Gomphonema* (175X)
(3) *Cymbella* (175X)
(4) *Cymbella* (1000X)
(5) *Gomphonema* (2000X)
(6) *Cocconeis* (750X)

(7) *Nitzschia* (1500X)
(8) *Pinnularia* (175X)
(9) *Cyclotella* (1000X)
(10) *Tabellaria* (175X)
(11) *Tabellaria* (1000X)
(12) *Synedra* (350X)

(13) *Synedra* (175X)
(14) *Melosira* (750X)
(15) *Surirella* (350X)
(16) *Stauroneis* (350X)
(17) *Fragillaria* (750X)
(18) *Fragillaria* (750X)

(19) *Asterionella* (175X)
(20) *Asterionella* (750X)
(21) *Navicula* (750X)
(22) *Stephanodiscus* (750X)
(23) *Meridion* (750X)

Figure 5.5   Diatoms.
(Courtesy of the U.S. Environmental Protection Agency, Office of Research & Development, Cincinnati, OH 45268)

Protozoa, Algae, and Cyanobacteria   ▌ EXERCISE 5

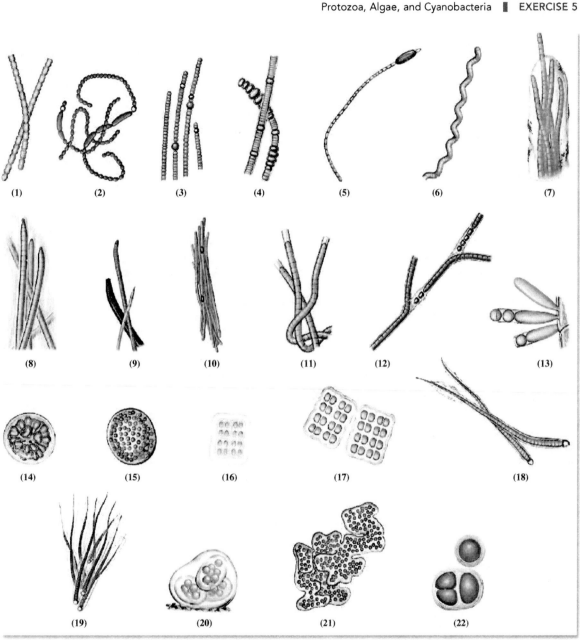

(1) *Anabaena* (350X)
(2) *Anabaena* (350X)
(3) *Anabaena* (175X)
(4) *Nodularia* (350X)
(5) *Cylindrospermum* (175X)
(6) *Arthrospira* (700X)

(7) *Microcoleus* (350X)
(8) *Phormidium* (350X)
(9) *Oscillatoria* (175X)
(10) *Aphanizomenon* (175X)
(11) *Lyngbya* (700X)
(12) *Tolypothrix* (350X)

(13) *Entophysalis* (1000X)
(14) *Gomphosphaeria* (1000X)
(15) *Gomphosphaeria* (350X)
(16) *Agmenellum* (700X)
(17) *Agmenellum* (175X)
(18) *Calothrix* (350X)

(19) *Rivularia* (175X)
(20) *Anacystis* (700X)
(21) *Anacystis* (175X)
(22) *Anacystis* (700X)

Figure 5.6   Cyanobacteria.
(Courtesy of the U.S. Environmental Protection Agency, Office of Research & Development, Cincinnati, OH 45268)

Microbiology, 11th Edition,
Short Version

EXERCISE 5 ▌ Protozoa, Algae, and Cyanobacteria

for "red tides" when great numbers of cells form spectacular blooms in the water, usually in response to a sudden influx of nutrients. The color of red tides can vary from intense red to orange to shades of brown depending on the number of cells present per volume of water and what plastid pigments are present. Red tides contain toxins that are produced by the dinoflagellates and stored in shellfish that ingest dinoflagellates and, thus, biologically magnify the toxin. These toxins can kill fish and other organisms, including humans, that eat the shellfish. Some dinoflagellates are heterotrophic; others are photosynthetic and contain chlorophylls a and c, fucoxanthin, peridinin, and several accessory pigments. Their chloroplasts are surrounded by three membranes and are thus very different from those of green plants. Dinoflagellates store a form of starch as an energy reserve. Zooxanthellae are certain species of dinoflagellates that are vital to healthy coral reefs in that they have an intimate endosymbiotic relationship with the coral. Storage molecules in dinoflagellates are diverse (e.g., oil, starch, and fat).

Prokaryotes

The Cyanobacteria

Cyanobacteria were once called "blue-green algae." Cyanobacteria have chlorophyll a and release oxygen during photosynthesis. They do not have an organized nucleus, chloroplasts, or other organelles. They do have peptidoglycan in their cell walls, hence they are prokaryotes. They differ from the green sulfur and the purple sulfur bacteria in that the latter use bacteriochlorophyll for photosynthesis and do not evolve oxygen because their photosynthetic metabolism is carried out under anaerobic conditions.

Over a thousand species of cyanobacteria have been described. Some representatives are depicted in figure 5.6. They are present in almost all moist environments from the tropics to the poles, in both marine and freshwater habitats. Cyanobacteria can be unicellular, colonial, or filamentous. Figure 5.6 illustrates only a random few that are frequently seen.

The designation of these bacteria as "blue-green" is somewhat misleading in that many are black, purple, red, and various shades of green, including blue-green. The varying colors are due to the varying proportions of photosynthetic pigments present, which include chlorophyll a, carotenoids, and phycobiliproteins. The latter pigments consist of allophycocyanin, phycocyanin, and phycoerythrin, that combine with protein molecules to form phycobilisomes, which serve as light harvesters for photosystems. These structures are also found in red algae. Because chloroplasts are not present, cyanobacteria use thylakoids as their photosynthetic apparatus. The phycobilisomes are attached to the thylakoids in parallel arrays.

Microbiology, 11th Edition,
Short Version

Protozoa, Algae, and Cyanobacteria (continued)

C. Fill-in-the-Blanks Questions

1. For each type of organism, place a check mark in the box to indicate whether the cellular characteristic or function is present.

CHARACTERISTIC OR FUNCTION	PROTOZOA	ALGAE	CYANOBACTERIA
Nucleus			
Flagella			
Pseudopodia			
Cilia			
Photosynthetic pigment(s)			
Chloroplasts			
Cell wall			

2. For each classification of protozoa, place a check mark in the box to indicate whether the cellular characteristic or function is present.

CHARACTERISTIC OR FUNCTION	AMOEBOID CELLS	FLAGELLATES	CILIATES	DIATOMS
Flagella				
Cilia				
Pseudopodia				
Gliding				
All members are parasitic				

Microbiology, 11th Edition,
Short Version

Protozoa, Algae, and Cyanobacteria (continued)

3. For each group name, place a check mark in the box to indicate whether the cellular characteristic or function is present.

	CHLORO-PLASTIDA	CHRYSO-PHYCEAE	EUGLENO-ZOA	PHAEO-PHYCEAE	BACCILARIO-PHYTA	DINO-FLAGELLATES (ALVEOLATA)	CYANO-BACTERIA

Pigments

Chlorophyll a							
Chlorophyll b							
Chlorophyll c							
Fucoxanthin							
c-phycocyanin							
c-phycoerythrin							

Cell Features

Flagella							
Cell wall							
Chloroplasts							

Food Storage

Starch							
Paramylon							
Leucosin							
Laminarin							
Oils							
Mannitol							

The Fungi:
Molds and Yeasts

7

The fungi comprise large groups of **heterotrophic** (non-photosynthesizing) **eukaryotic** organisms that produce exoenzymes and absorb their nutrients (**osmotrophic**). Fungi may be saprophytic or parasitic. They may be unicellular or filamentous. The distinguishing characteristics of the group as a whole is that they are (1) eukaryotic, (2) heterotrophic, (3) lack tissue differentiation, (4) have cell walls of chitin or other polysaccharides, and (5) propagate by spores (sexual and/or asexual).

Many diverse organisms have been traditionally categorized as fungi, including water molds, mushrooms, puffballs, bracket fungi, yeasts and molds. These organisms do not have a uniform genetic background, and are believed to have evolved from at least two ancestral lineages. Classification of fungi is a complex and dynamic process. Traditional classification schemes rely primarily on morphological characteristics and reproductive mechanisms to categorize fungal groups. More modern schemes use genetic analysis to determine relatedness between species and subsequent categorization. Recently collected data from genetic analyses of fungi indicate that fungal classification based on morphology does not necessarily reflect evolutionary relationships between organisms. However, identification and categorization of fungal types are still most easily performed in the introductory laboratory using morphological characteristics. In this exercise, we will examine prepared stained slides and slides made from living cultures of yeasts and molds. Molds are normally present in the air and can be cultured and studied macroscopically and microscopically. In addition, an attempt will be made to identify the various fungal types that are cultured based on morphological characteristics.

Before attempting to identify the various molds, familiarize yourself with the basic differences between molds and yeasts. Note in figure 7.1 that yeasts are essentially unicellular and molds are multicellular.

Fungi

Fungal forms: molds and yeasts

Molds   Molds are fungi that contain microscopic intertwining filaments called *hyphae* (*hypha*, singular). A mass of hyphae forms the **mycelium** that is

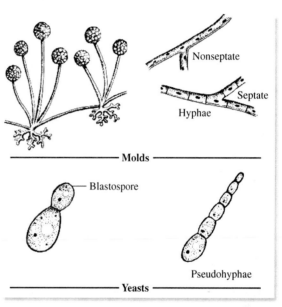

Figure 7.1 Structural differences between molds and yeasts.

seen macroscopically as the fungal colony. As shown in figure 7.1, **septa** or crosswalls separate the hyphae of some fungi into individual compartments with an organized nucleus and organelles. In most fungi, the septa have central openings or pores that allow for the streaming of cytoplasm between compartments. If no crosswalls are present, the hyphae are said to be nonseptate or **coenocytic.** A mass of intermeshed hyphae, as seen macroscopically, is a *mycelium.*

Yeasts   Yeasts are fungi that lack hyphae. These fungi multiply by budding or fission or a combination of these two processes. As shown in figure 7.1, yeast cells may form chains of buds called **pseudohyphae.**

Some species of fungi occur exclusively as molds, while other species occur exclusively as yeasts. A number of fungal species, known as **dimorphic** fungi, can occur as either molds or yeasts, depending on environmental conditions.

Fungal spores: asexual and sexual

Fungal spores are important in the reproductive cycle and can be produced through either asexual or sexual

Microbiology, 11th Edition,
Short Version

EXERCISE 7 ▌ The Fungi

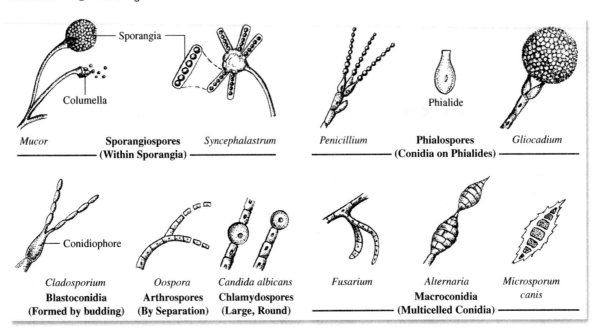

Figure 7.2 Types of asexual spores seen in fungi.

means. There is great variation in spore size, color, and appearance between species. Much of the traditional taxonomy of fungi is based on morphological characteristics of spores and spore-related structures. In this exercise, you will attempt to identify fungi based, in part, on these characteristics.

Asexual spores Fungi produce asexual spores by mitotic division of a parental cell. Asexual spore formation does not involve the union of cell nuclei. Two types of asexual spores are sporangiospores and conidia. Both types are shown in figure 7.2.

  Sporangiospores: Sporangiospores are asexual spores that form *within* a thin-walled sac called a sporangium. Sporangiospores can be motile or non-motile.
  Conidia: Conidia are asexual non-motile spores that form on specialized hyphae called conidiophores. Several different categories of conidia exist. They include Phialospores, Blastospores, Arthrospores, and Chlamydospores.
  Phialospores: are asexual reproductive spores produced from a vase or flask-shaped cell called a phialide. *Penicillium* and *Gliocadium* produce this type.
  Blastospores: are asexual reproductive spores produced by budding from cells in yeast and some filamentous fungi (molds). *Cladosporium* and *Candida* are examples

of genera that reproduce asexually by blastospores.
  Arthrospores: are asexual reproductive spores produced by fragmentation of preexisting hyphae. *Geotrichum* and *Galactomyces* produce this type of spore.
  Chlamydospores: are thick-walled, round or irregular asexual spores whose function is survival. These are common to most fungi.

Sexual spores Fungi produce sexual spores by the union of two parental nuclei followed by meiotic division. Three kinds of sexual spores are seen in fungi. These are the zygospores, ascospores, and basidiospores. Figure 7.3 illustrates these three types.

  Zygospores: are formed by the union of nuclear material from the hyphae of two different gametangia (+, −) which appear morpholically identical but are genetically different.
  Ascospores: are haploid sexual spores formed in the interior of an oval or elongated enclosure usually termed an ascus.
  Basidiospores: are sexual haploid spores produced externally on a club-shaped basidium.

Yeasts

Hyphae Unicellular fungi multiply by budding or fission or by a combination of the two processes (figure 7.1).

Microbiology, 11th Edition, Short Version

The Fungi ❚ EXERCISE 7

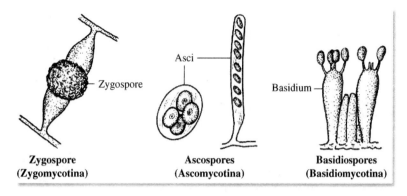

Figure 7.3   Types of sexual spores seen in the Amastigomycota.

Subdivision of the Kingdom Eumycota

The Kingdom Eumycota is made up of three phyla: Chytridiomycota, Zygomycota, and the Dikaryomycota.

The **Chytridiomycota** are aquatic organisms that vary morphologically and may be unicellular or filamentous. Asexual reproduction generates zoospores with one whiplash flagellum.

The **Zygomycota** prefer an atmosphere with high relative humidity and produce coencytic hyphae that are wide and thin-walled. They are coenocytic, having no crosswalls. This phylum reproduces sexually by fusion of gametangia, forming a zygospore, and asexually by non-motile sporangiospores.

The **Dikaryomycota** contain the most species diversity and are divided into the subphyla **Ascomycotina** and **Basidiomycotina.** The Dikaryomycota contain chitin in their cell walls, have hyphae with septa, and their hyphae fuse and exchange nuclei **(anastomosis).** In a phase of their life cycle, the hyphae can contain two haploid nuclei in each cell **(dikaryon).**

Ascomycotina produce ascospores in an ascus and they are commonly referred to as the "sac fungi," or ascomycetes. Ascomycotina produce ascospores in one of the following structures:

Apothecia: A cup or dish-shaped fruiting body that opens widely to expose the asci-containing ascospores.
Perithecia: Flask-shaped fruiting structures containing asci with ascospores.
Cleithothecia: Enclosed ascocarps that lack a pore-containing asci with ascospores.

Basidiomycotina produce basidiospores 1, 2, or 4 externally on a basidium. These are the puffballs, mushrooms, smuts, rusts, and shelf fungi.

In zygomycetes, the anamorph and telemorph stages often occur at the same time. However, in ascomycetes and basidiomycetes these stages do not occur simultaneously but appear at different times

on different substrates. The International Code of Botanical Nomenclature thus stipulates that a different genus-species name for each stage is an accepted practice. However, as the anamorph and telemorph stages are identified as the same fungus, the organism is referred to by the telemorph or sexual stage binomial name. The anamorph stage fungi are often classed as the imperfect fungi, or deuteromycetes. There are more than 15,000 species in this group.

Laboratory Procedures

Several options are provided here for the study of fungi. The procedures to be followed will be outlined by your instructor.

Yeast Study

The organism *Saccharomyces cerevisiae,* which is used in bread making and alcohol fermentation, will be used for this study. Either prepared slides or living organisms may be used.

Materials

- prepared slides of *Saccharomyces cerevisiae*
- broth cultures of *Saccharomyces cerevisiae*
- methylene blue stain
- microscope slides and coverslips

Prepared Slides   If prepared slides are used, they may be examined under high-dry or oil immersion. Look for typical **blastospores** and **ascospores.** Space is provided on the Laboratory Report for drawing the organisms.

Living Materials   If broth cultures of *Saccharomyces cerevisiae* are available, they should be examined on a wet mount slide with phase-contrast or brightfield optics. Place two or three loopfuls of the

Microbiology, 11th Edition,
Short Version

EXERCISE 7 ▌ The Fungi

organisms on the slide with a drop of methylene blue stain. Oil immersion will reveal the greatest amount of detail. Look for the **nucleus** and **vacuole.** The nucleus is the smaller body. Draw a few cells on the Laboratory Report.

Fungi Study

Examine a petri plate of Sabouraud's agar that has been exposed to the air for about an hour and incubated at room temperature for 3–5 days. This medium has a low pH, which makes it selective for fungi. A good plate will have many different-colored colonies. Note the characteristic "cottony" nature of the colonies. Also, look at the bottom of the plate and observe how the colonies differ in color here. Colony surface color, underside pigmentation, hyphal structure, and the type of spores produced are important phenotypic characteristics used in the identification of fungi.

Figure 7.4 reveals how some common molds appear when grown on Sabouraud's agar. Keep in mind that the appearance of a fungal colony can change appreciably as it gets older. The photographs in figure 7.4 are of colonies that are 10 to 21 days old.

Conclusive identification cannot be made unless a microscope slide is made to determine the type of hyphae and spores that are present. Figure 7.5 reveals, diagrammatically, the microscopic differences to look for when identifying fungal genera.

Two Options   In making slides from fungal colonies, one can make either wet mounts directly from the colonies by the procedure outlined here or make cultured slides as outlined in Exercise 22. The following steps should be used for making stained slides directly from the colonies. Your instructor will indicate the number of identifications that are to be made.

Materials

- fungal cultures on Sabouraud's agar
- microscope slides and coverslips
- lactophenol cotton blue stain
- sharp-pointed scalpels or dissecting needles

1. Place an uncovered plate on a dissecting microscope and examine the colony. Look for hyphal structures and spore arrangement. Increase the magnification if necessary to more clearly see spores. Ignore white colonies as they are usually young and have not begun the sporulation process.

2. Consult figures 7.4 and 7.5 to make a preliminary identification based on colony characteris-

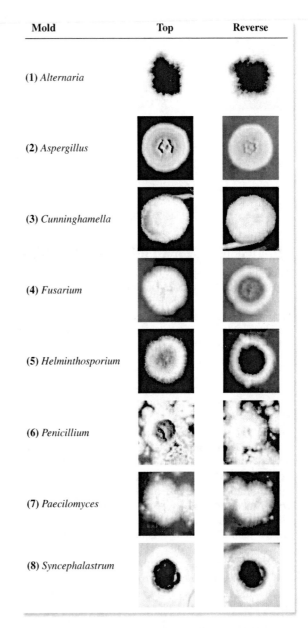

Mold	Top	Reverse
(1) *Alternaria*		
(2) *Aspergillus*		
(3) *Cunninghamella*		
(4) *Fusarium*		
(5) *Helminthosporium*		
(6) *Penicillium*		
(7) *Paecilomyces*		
(8) *Syncephalastrum*		

Figure 7.4   Colony characteristics of some of the more common molds.

tics and low-power magnification of hyphae and spores.

3. Make a wet mount slide by transferring a small amount of mycelium with a scalpel, dissecting needle, or toothpick to a drop of lactophenol cotton blue. Gently tease apart the mycelium with the dissecting needles. Cover the specimen with a coverslip and examine with the low-power objective. Look for hyphae that have spore structures.

The Fungi ▮ EXERCISE 7

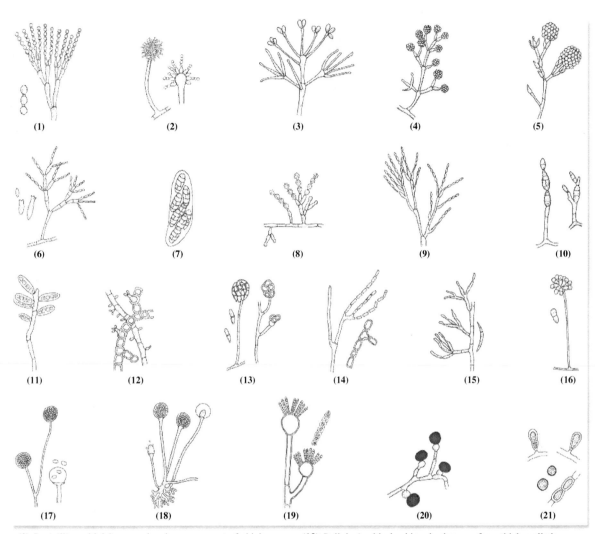

(1)   (2)   (3)   (4)   (5)

(6)   (7)   (8)   (9)   (10)

(11)   (12)   (13)   (14)   (15)   (16)

(17)   (18)   (19)   (20)   (21)

(1) *Penicillium*– bluish-green; brush arrangement of phialospores.

(2) *Aspergillus*– bluish-green with sulfur-yellow areas on the surface. *Aspergillus niger* is black.

(3) *Verticillium*– pinkish-brown, elliptical microconidia.

(4) *Trichoderma*– green, resemble *Penicillium* macroscopically.

(5) *Gliocadium*– dark-green; conidia (phialospores) borne on phialides, similar to *Penicillium*; grows faster than *Penicillium*.

(6) *Cladosporium (Hormodendrum)*– light green to grayish surface; gray to black back surface; blastoconidia.

(7) *Pleospora*– tan to green surface with brown to black back; ascospores shown are produced in sacs borne within brown, flask-shaped fruiting bodies called pseudothecia.

(8) *Scopulariopsis*– light-brown; rough-walled microconidia.

(9) *Paecilomyces*– yellowish-brown, elliptical microconidia.

(10) *Alternaria*– dark greenish-black surface with gray periphery; black on reverse side; chains of macroconidia.

(11) *Bipolaris*– black surface with grayish periphery; macroconidia shown.

(12) *Pullularia*– black, shiny, leathery surface; thick-walled; budding spores.

(13) *Diplosporium*– buff-colored wooly surface; reverse side has red center surrounded by brown.

(14) *Oospora (Geotrichum)*– buff-colored surface; hyphae break up into thin-walled rectangular arthrospores.

(15) *Fusarium*– variants, of yellow, orange, red, and purple colonies; sickle-shaped macroconidia.

(16) *Trichothecium*– white to pink surface; two-celled conidia.

(17) *Mucor*– a zygomycete; sporangia with a slimy texture; spores with dark pigment.

(18) *Rhizopus*– a zygomycete; spores with dark pigment.

(19) *Syncephalastrum*– a zygomycete; sporangiophores bear rod-shaped sporangioles, each containing a row of spherical spores.

(20) *Nigrospora*– conidia black, globose, one-celled, borne on a flattened, colorless vesicle at the end of a conidiophore.

(21) *Montospora*– dark gray center with light gray periphery; yellow-brown conidia.

Figure 7.5   **Microscopic appearance of some of the more common molds.**

Microbiology, 11th Edition,
Short Version

EXERCISE 7 ▐ The Fungi

Go to the high-dry objective to discern more detail about the spores. Compare your specimen to figure 7.5 and see if you can identify the culture based on microscopic morphology.

4. Repeat the procedure for each colony.

Note: An alternative procedure that preserves the fruiting structures is the **cellophane tape method.** Place 1–2 drops of lactophenol cotton blue on a microscope slide. Using a piece of *clear* cellophane tape slightly smaller than the length of the slide, gently touch the surface of a fungal colony with the sticky side of the tape. Transfer the tape containing the material from the fungal colony to the lactophenol cotton blue stain and press the tape onto the slide, making sure that the culture material is in the stain. Observe with the low-power and high-dry lens.

Laboratory Report

After recording your results on the Laboratory Report, answer all the questions.

Manipulation of Microorganisms

One of the most critical techniques that any beginning student in microbiology must learn is aseptic technique. This technique insures that an aseptic environment is maintained when handling microorganisms. This means two things:

1. no contaminating microorganisms are introduced into cultures or culture materials and
2. the microbiologist is not contaminated by cultures that are being manipulated.

Aseptic technique is crucial in characterizing an unknown organism. Oftentimes, multiple transfers must be made from a stock culture to various test media. It is imperative that only the desired organism is transferred each time and that no foreign bacteria are introduced during the transfer. Aseptic technique is also obligatory in isolating and purifying bacteria from a mixed source of organisms. The streak-plate and pour-plate techniques provide a means to isolate an individual species. And once an organism is in pure culture and stored as a stock culture, aseptic technique insures that the culture remains pure when it is necessary to retrieve the organism.

Individuals who work with pathogenic bacteria must be sure that any pathogen that is being handled is not accidently released causing harm to themselves or to coworkers. Failure to observe aseptic technique can obviously pose a serious threat to many.

In the following exercises, you will learn the techniques that allow you to handle and manipulate cultures of microorganisms. Once you have mastered these procedures, you will be able to make transfers of microorganisms from one kind of medium to another with confidence. You will also be able to isolate an organism from a mixed culture to obtain a pure isolate. It is imperative that you have a good grasp of these procedures, as they will be required over and over in the exercises in this manual.

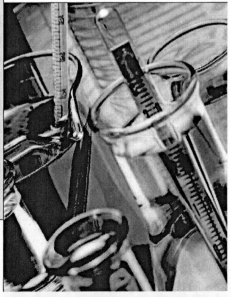

Aseptic Technique

exercise

8

The use of aseptic technique insures that no contaminating organisms are introduced into culture materials when the latter are inoculated or handled in some manner. It also insures that organisms that are being handled do not contaminate the handler or others who may be present. And its use means that no contamination remains after you have worked with cultures.

As you work with these procedures, with time, they will become routine and second nature to you. You will automatically know that a set of procedures outlined below will be used when dealing with cultures of microorganisms. This may involve the transfer of a broth culture to a plate for streaking, or inoculating an isolated colony from a plate onto a slant culture to prepare a stock culture. It may also involve inoculating many tubes of media and agar plates from a stock culture in order to characterize and identify an unknown bacterium. Ensuring that only the desired organism is transferred in each inoculation is of paramount importance in the identification process. The general procedure for aseptic technique follows.

Work Area Disinfection   The work area is first treated with a disinfectant to kill any microorganisms that may be present. This process destroys vegetative cells and viruses but may not destroy endospores.

Loops and Needles   The transfer of cultures will be achieved using inoculating loops and needles. These implements must be sterilized before transferring any culture. A loop or needle is sterilized by inserting it into a Bunsen burner flame until it is red-hot. This will incinerate any contaminating organisms that may be present. Allow the loop to cool completely before picking up inoculum. This will ensure that viable cells are transferred.

Culture Tube Flaming and Inoculation   Prior to inserting a cooled loop or needle into a culture tube, the cap is removed and the mouth of the tube is flamed. If the tube is a broth tube, the loop is inserted into the tube and twisted several times to ensure that the organisms on the loop are delivered to the liquid. If the tube is an agar slant, the surface of the slant is inoculated by drawing the loop up the surface of the slant from the bottom of the slant to its top. For stab

cultures, a needle is inserted into the agar medium by stabbing it into the agar. After the culture is inoculated, the mouth of the tube is reflamed and the tube is recapped.

Final Flaming of the Loop or Needle   After the inoculation is complete, the loop or needle is flamed in the Bunsen burner to destroy any organisms that remain on these implements. The loop or needle is then returned to its receptacle for storage. It should never be placed on the desk surface.

Petri Plate Inoculations   Loops are used to inoculate or streak petri plates. The plate cover is raised and held diagonally over the plate to protect the surface from any contamination in the air. The loop containing the inoculum is then streaked gently over the surface of the agar. It is important not to gouge or disturb the surface of the agar with the loop. The cover is replaced and the loop is flamed in a Bunsen burner.

Final Disinfection of the Work Area   When all work for the day is complete, the work area is treated with disinfectant to insure that any organism that might have been deposited during any of the procedures is killed.

To gain some practice in aseptic transfer of bacterial cultures, three simple transfers will be performed in this exercise:
1. broth culture to broth tube
2. agar slant culture to an agar slant and
3. agar plate to an agar slant.

Transfer from Broth Culture to Another Broth

Do a broth tube to broth tube inoculation using the following technique. Figure 8.1 illustrates the procedure for removing organisms from a culture, and figure 8.2 shows how to inoculate a tube of sterile broth.

Materials

- broth culture of *Escherichia coli*
- tubes of sterile nutrient broth
- inoculating loop

**Microbiology, 11th Edition,
Short Version**

EXERCISE 8   ▌   Aseptic Technique

- Bunsen burner
- disinfectant for desktop and sponge
- Sharpie marking pen

1. Prepare your desktop by swabbing down its surface with a disinfectant. Use a sponge or paper towels.
2. With a marking pen, label a tube of sterile nutrient broth with your initials and *E. coli.*
3. Sterilize your inoculating loop by holding it over the flame of a Bunsen burner **until it becomes bright red.** The entire wire must be heated. See illustration 1, figure 8.1.
4. Using your free hand, gently shake the tube to disperse the culture (illustration 2, figure 8.1).
5. Grasp the tube cap with the little finger of your hand holding the inoculating loop and remove it from the tube. Flame the mouth of the tube as shown in illustration 3, figure 8.1.
6. Insert the inoculating loop into the culture (illustration 4, figure 8.1).

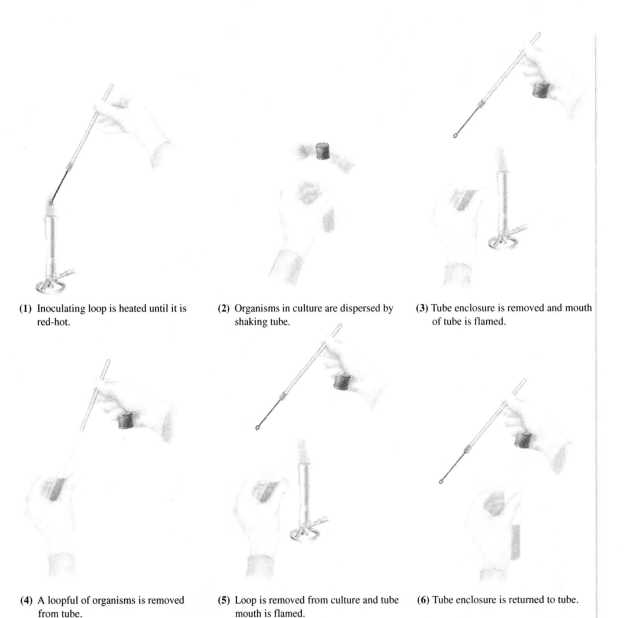

(1) Inoculating loop is heated until it is red-hot.

(2) Organisms in culture are dispersed by shaking tube.

(3) Tube enclosure is removed and mouth of tube is flamed.

(4) A loopful of organisms is removed from tube.

(5) Loop is removed from culture and tube mouth is flamed.

(6) Tube enclosure is returned to tube.

Figure 8.1   Procedure for removing organisms from a broth culture with inoculating loop.

Aseptic Technique ▌ EXERCISE 8

7. Remove the loop containing the culture, flame the mouth of the tube again (illustration 5, figure 8.1), and recap the tube (illustration 6). Place the culture tube back on the test-tube rack.

8. Grasp a tube of sterile nutrient broth with your free hand, carefully remove the cap with your little finger, and flame the mouth of this tube (illustration 1, figure 8.2).

9. Without flaming the loop, insert it into the sterile broth, inoculating it (illustration 2, figure 8.2). To disperse the organisms into the medium, move the loop back and forth in the tube.

10. Remove the loop from the tube and flame the mouth (illustration 3, figure 8.2). Replace the cap on the tube (illustration 4, figure 8.2).

11. Sterilize the loop by flaming it (illustration 5, figure 8.2). Return the loop to its container.

12. Incubate the culture you just inoculated at 37° C for 24–48 hours.

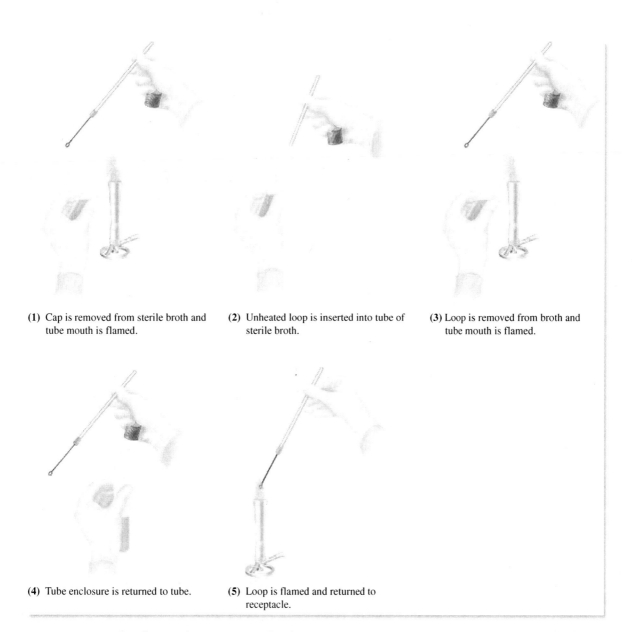

(1) Cap is removed from sterile broth and tube mouth is flamed.

(2) Unheated loop is inserted into tube of sterile broth.

(3) Loop is removed from broth and tube mouth is flamed.

(4) Tube enclosure is returned to tube.

(5) Loop is flamed and returned to receptacle.

Figure 8.2   Procedure for inoculating a nutrient broth.

Microbiology, 11th Edition,
Short Version

EXERCISE 8 ▍ Aseptic Technique

Transfer of Bacteria from a Slant

To inoculate a sterile nutrient agar slant from an agar slant culture, use the following procedure. Figure 8.3 illustrates the entire process.

Materials

- agar slant culture of *E. coli*
- sterile nutrient agar slant
- inoculating loop
- Bunsen burner
- Sharpie marking pen

1. If you have not already done so, prepare your desktop by swabbing down its surface with a disinfectant.
2. With a marking pen label a tube of nutrient agar slant with your initials and *E. coli.*
3. Sterilize your inoculating loop by holding it over the flame of a Bunsen burner *until it become bright red* (illustration 1, figure 8.3). The entire wire must be heated. Allow the loop to cool completely.
4. Using your free hand, pick up the slant culture of *E. coli* and remove the cap using the little finger of the hand that is holding the loop (illustration 2, figure 8.3).
5. Flame the mouth of the tube and insert the cooled loop into the tube. Pick up some of the culture on the loop (illustration 3, figure 8.3) and remove the loop from the tube.

6. Flame the mouth of the tube (illustrations 4 and 5, figure 8.3) and replace the cap, being careful not to burn your hand. Return tube to rack.
7. Pick up a sterile nutrient agar slant with your free hand, remove the cap with your little finger as before, and flame the mouth of the tube (illustration 6, figure 8.3).
8. Without flaming the loop containing the culture, insert the loop into the tube and gently inoculate the surface of the slant by moving the loop back and forth over the agar surface, while moving up the surface of the slant (illustration 7, figure 8.3). This should involve a type of serpentine or zig-zag motion.
9. Remove the loop, flame the mouth of the tube, and recap the tube (illustration 8, figure 8.3). Replace the tube in the rack.
10. Flame the loop, heating the entire wire to red-hot (illustration 9, figure 8.3), allow to cool, and place the loop in its container.
11. Incubate the inoculated agar slant at 30° C for 24–48 hours.

Working with Agar Plates

(Inoculating a slant from a petri plate)

The transfer of organisms from colonies on agar plates to slants or broth tubes is very similar to the procedures used in the last two transfers (broth to broth and slant to slant). The following rules should be observed.

 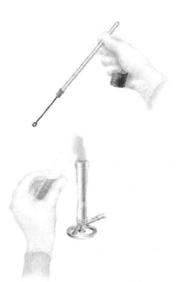 

(1) Inoculating loop is heated until it is red-hot.

(2) Cap is removed from slant culture and tube mouth is heated.

(3) Organism is picked up from slant with inoculating loop.

continued

Figure 8.3 Procedure for inoculating a nutrient agar slant from a slant culture.

Microbiology, 11th Edition,
Short Version

Aseptic Technique ▌ EXERCISE 8

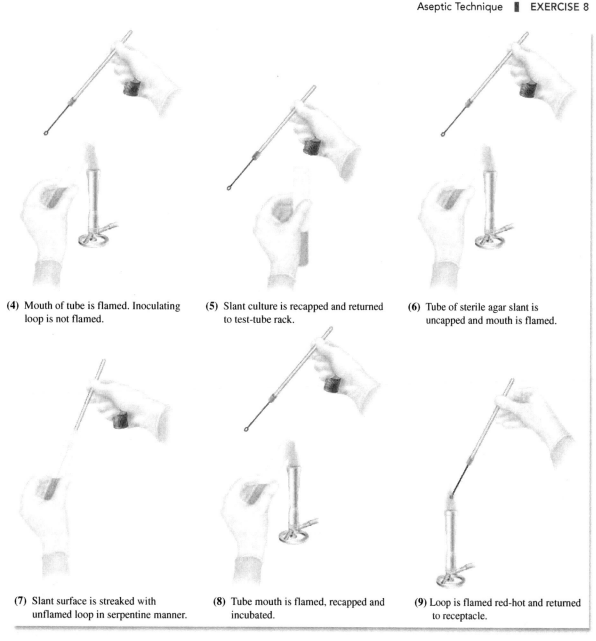

(4) Mouth of tube is flamed. Inoculating loop is not flamed.

(5) Slant culture is recapped and returned to test-tube rack.

(6) Tube of sterile agar slant is uncapped and mouth is flamed.

(7) Slant surface is streaked with unflamed loop in serpentine manner.

(8) Tube mouth is flamed, recapped and incubated.

(9) Loop is flamed red-hot and returned to receptacle.

Figure 8.3 *(continued)*

Loops and Needles Loops are routinely used when streaking agar plates and slants. When used properly, a loop will not gouge or tear the agar surface. Needles are used in transfers involving stab cultures.

Plate Handling Media in plates must always be protected against contamination. To prevent exposure to air contamination, covers should always be left closed. When organisms are removed from a plate culture, the cover should be only partially opened as shown in illustration 2, figure 8.4.

Flaming Procedures Inoculating loops or needles must be flamed in the same manner that you used when working with previous tubes. One difference when working with plates is that plates are never flamed!

Plate Labeling and Incubation Petri plates containing inoculated media are labeled on the bottom of the plate. Inoculated plates are almost always incubated upside down. This prevents moisture from condensing on the agar surface and spreading the inoculated organisms.

Microbiology, 11th Edition,
Short Version

EXERCISE 8 ▌ Aseptic Technique

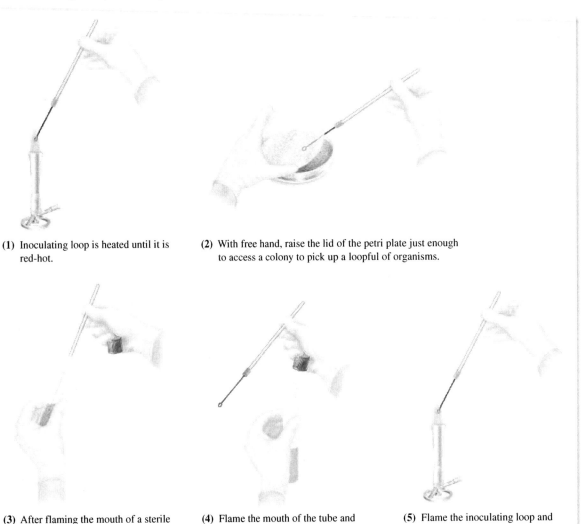

(1) Inoculating loop is heated until it is red-hot.

(2) With free hand, raise the lid of the petri plate just enough to access a colony to pick up a loopful of organisms.

(3) After flaming the mouth of a sterile slant, streak its surface.

(4) Flame the mouth of the tube and recap the tube.

(5) Flame the inoculating loop and return it to receptacle.

Figure 8.4 Procedure for inoculating a nutrient agar slant from an agar plate.

To transfer organisms from a petri plate to an agar slant, use the following procedure:

Materials

- nutrient agar plate with bacterial colonies
- sterile nutrient agar slant
- inoculating loop
- Sharpie marking pen

1. If you have not done so, swab your work area with disinfectant. Allow area to dry.
2. Label a sterile nutrient agar slant with your name and organism to be transferred.
3. Flame an inoculating loop until it is red-hot (illustration 1, figure 8.4). Allow the loop to cool.
4. As shown in illustration 2, figure 8.4, raise the lid of a petri plate sufficiently to access a colony with your sterile loop.
   Do not gouge into the agar with your loop as you pick up organisms, and do not completely remove the lid, exposing the surface to the air. Close the lid once you have picked up the organisms.
5. With your free hand, pick up the sterile nutrient agar slant tube. Remove the cap by grasping the cap with the little finger of the hand that is holding the loop.

Aseptic Technique ▐ EXERCISE 8

6. Flame the mouth of the tube and insert the loop into the tube to inoculate the surface of the slant, using a serpentine motion (illustration 3, figure 8.4). Avoid disrupting the agar surface with the loop.
7. Remove the loop from the tube and flame the mouth of the tube. Replace the cap on the tube (illustration 4, figure 8.4).

8. Flame the loop (illustration 5, figure 8.4) and place it in its container.
9. Incubate the nutrient agar slant at 37° C for 24–48 hours.

Second Period

Examine all three tubes and record your results in Laboratory Report 8.

8

Laboratory Report

Student: _____

Date: _____   Section: _____

8   Aseptic Technique

A. Results

1. Were all your transfers successful? _____

2. What evidence do you have that they were successful? _____

   _____

3. What evidence do you have that a transfer is unsuccessful? _____

   _____

B. Short Answer Questions

1. Provide three reasons why the use of aseptic technique is essential when handling microbial cultures in the laboratory.

   _____

   _____

2. Provide two examples of how the Bunsen burner is used during inoculation of a tube culture.

   _____

   _____

3. How is air contamination prevented when an inoculating loop is used to introduce or take a bacterial sample to/from an agar plate?

   _____

   _____

4. Where should a label be written on an agar plate?

   _____

   _____

5. How should agar plates be incubated? Why?

   _____

   _____

6. Against which organisms are disinfectants effective? Against which type of organism may they not be effective? What disinfectant(s) is used in your laboratory?

   _____

   _____

Microbiology, 11th Edition,
Short Version

Aseptic Technique (continued)

C. Multiple Choice Questions

Select the answer that best completes the following statements.

1. A disinfectant is used on your work surface
   a. before the beginning of laboratory procedures.
   b. after all work is complete.
   c. after any spill of live microorganisms.
   d. Both (b) and (c) are correct.
   e. All of the above are correct.

2. To retrieve a sample from a culture tube with an inoculating loop, the cap of the tube is
   a. removed and held in one's teeth.
   b. removed and held with the fingers of the loop hand.
   c. removed with the fingers of the loop hand and placed in the fingers of the tube hand.
   d. removed with the fingers of the loop hand and placed on the laboratory bench.
   e. Any of these methods can be used.

3. An inoculating loop or needle is sterilized in a flame
   a. by one brief passage.
   b. for exactly 5 minutes.
   c. until it is entirely bright red.
   d. until the handle is bright red.
   e. until the tip is bright red.

ANSWERS

Multiple Choice

1. _____

2. _____

3. _____

Staining and Observation of Microorganisms

PART

4

The eight exercises in this unit include the procedures for ten slide techniques that one might employ in morphological studies of bacteria. A culture method in Exercise 17 also is included as a substitute for slide techniques when pathogens are encountered.

These exercises are intended to serve two equally important functions: (1) to help you to develop the necessary skills in making slides and (2) to introduce you to the morphology of bacteria. Although the title of each exercise pertains to a specific technique, the organisms chosen for each method have been carefully selected so that you can learn to recognize certain morphological features. For example, in the exercise on simple staining (Exercise 11), a single staining procedure applied to the selected organism can be used to demonstrate cell morphology, cell arrangement, and internal storage materials such as metachromatic granules. In Exercise 14 (Gram Staining), you will learn how to perform an important differential stain that employs more than one stain. This procedure allows you to taxonomically differentiate between two different kinds of bacteria as well as distinguish their cell morphology—cocci or rods.

The importance of the mastery of these techniques cannot be overemphasized. Although one is seldom able to make species identification on the basis of morphological characteristics alone, it is a very significant starting point. This fact will become increasingly clear with subsequent experiments.

Although the steps in the various staining procedures may seem relatively simple, student success is often quite unpredictable. Unless your instructor suggests a variation in the procedure, try to follow the procedures exactly as stated, without improvisation. Photomicrographs in color have been provided for many of the techniques; use them as a guide to evaluate the slides you have prepared. Once you have mastered a specific technique, feel free to experiment.

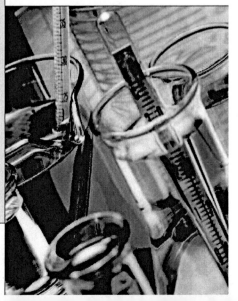

Read
intro

Smear Preparation

10

The success for most staining procedures depends upon the preparation of a good **smear.** There are several goals in preparing a smear. The first goal is to cause the cells to adhere to the microscope slide so that they are not washed off during subsequent staining and washing procedures. Second, it is important to insure that shrinkage of cells does not occur during staining, otherwise distortion and artifacts can result. A third goal is to prepare thin smears because the thickness of the smear will determine if you can visualize individual cells, their arrangement, or details regarding microstructures associated with cells. Thick smears of cells with large clumps obscure details about individual cells and, furthermore, the smear can entrap stain, keeping it from being removed by washing or destaining, leading to erroneous results. The procedure for making a smear is illustrated in figure 10.1.

The first step in preparing a bacteriological smear differs according to the source of the organisms. If the bacteria are growing in a liquid medium (broths, milk, saliva, urine, etc.), one starts by placing two or more loopfuls of the liquid medium directly on the slide.

From solid media such as nutrient agar, blood agar, or some part of the body, one starts by placing one or two loopfuls of water on the slide and then using an inoculating loop to disperse the organisms in the water. Bacteria growing on solid media tend to cling to each other and must be dispersed sufficiently by dilution in water; unless this is done, the smear will be too thick. *The most difficult concept for students to understand about making slides from solid media is that it takes only a very small amount of material to make a good smear.* When your instructor demonstrates this step, pay very careful attention to the amount of material that is placed on the slide.

The organisms to be used for your first slides may be from several different sources. If the plates from Exercise 6 were saved, some slides may be made from them. If they were discarded, the first slides may be made for Exercise 11, which pertains to

simple staining. Your instructor will indicate which cultures to use.

From Liquid Media

(Broths, saliva, milk, etc.)

If you are preparing a bacterial smear from liquid media, follow this routine, which is depicted on the left side of figure 10.1.

Materials

* microscope slides
* Bunsen burner
* wire loop
* Sharpie marking pen
* slide holder (clothespin)

1. Wash a slide with soap or Bon Ami and hot water, removing all dirt and grease. Handle the clean slide by its edges.
2. Write the initials of the organism or organisms on the left-hand side of the slide with a marking pen.
3. To provide a target on which to place the organisms, make a $\frac{1}{2}''$ circle on the *bottom* side of the slide, centrally located, with a marking pen. Later on, when you become more skilled, you may wish to omit the use of this "target circle."
4. Shake the culture vigorously and transfer two loopfuls of organisms to the center of the slide over the target circle. Follow the routine for inoculations shown in figure 10.2. *Be sure to flame the loop after it has touched the slide.*

> **CAUTION:** Be sure to cool the loop completely before inserting it into a medium. A loop that is too hot will spatter the medium and move bacteria into the air.

5. Spread the organisms over the area of the target circle.
6. Allow the slide to dry by normal evaporation of the water. Don't apply heat.

Microbiology, 11th Edition, Short Version

EXERCISE 10 ▌ Smear Preparation

7. After the smear has become completely dry, place the slide in a clothespin and pass it several times through the flame of a Bunsen burner. Avoid prolonged heating of the slide as it can shatter from excessive exposure to heat. The underside of the slide should feel warm to the touch.

Note that in this step one has the option of using or not using a clothespin to hold the slide. *Use the option preferred by your instructor.*

From Solid Media

When preparing a bacterial smear from solid media, such as nutrient agar or a part of the body, follow this routine, which is depicted on the right side of figure 10.1.

Materials

- microscope slides
- inoculating needle and loop

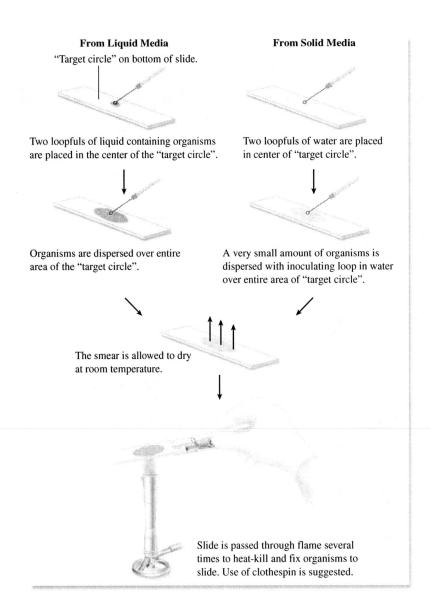

From Liquid Media

"Target circle" on bottom of slide.

Two loopfuls of liquid containing organisms are placed in the center of the "target circle".

Organisms are dispersed over entire area of the "target circle".

From Solid Media

Two loopfuls of water are placed in center of "target circle".

A very small amount of organisms is dispersed with inoculating loop in water over entire area of "target circle".

The smear is allowed to dry at room temperature.

Slide is passed through flame several times to heat-kill and fix organisms to slide. Use of clothespin is suggested.

Figure 10.1 Procedure for making a bacterial smear.

Smear Preparation ▮ EXERCISE 10

* Sharpie marking pen
* slide holder (clothespin)
* Bunsen burner

1. Wash a slide with soap or Bon Ami and hot water, removing all dirt and grease. Handle the clean slide by its edges.

2. Write the initials of the organism or organisms on the left-hand side of the slide with a marking pen.

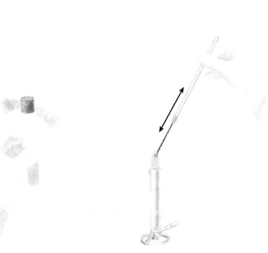
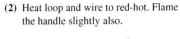

(1) Shake the culture tube from side to side to suspend organisms. Do not moisten cap on tube.

(2) Heat loop and wire to red-hot. Flame the handle slightly also.

(3) Remove the cap and flame the neck of the tube. Do not place the cap down on the table.

(4) After allowing the loop to cool for at least 5 seconds, remove a loopful of organisms. Avoid touching the side of the tube.

(5) Flame the mouth of the culture tube again.

(6) Return the cap to the tube and place the tube in a test-tube rack.

continued

Figure 10.2   Aseptic procedure for organism removal.

**Microbiology, 11th Edition,
Short Version**

EXERCISE 10 ▌ Smear Preparation

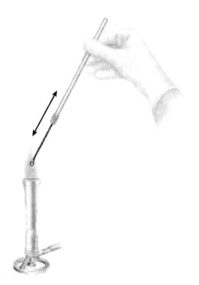

(7) Place the loopful of organisms in the center of the target circle on the slide.

(8) Flame the loop again before removing another loopful from the culture or setting the inoculating loop aside.

Figure 10.2 *(continued)*

3. Mark a "target circle" on the bottom side of the slide with a marking pen. (See comments in step 3 on page 87.)
4. Flame an inoculating loop, let it cool, and transfer two loopfuls of water to the center of the target circle.
5. Flame an inoculating needle then let it cool. Pick up *a very small amount of the organisms,* and mix it into the water on the slide. Disperse the mixture over the area of the target circle. Be certain that the organisms have been well emulsified in the liquid. *Be sure to flame the inoculating needle before placing it in its holder.*

6. Allow the slide to dry by normal evaporation of the water. Don't apply heat.
7. After the slide has become completely dry, place it in a clothespin and pass it several times through the flame of a Bunsen burner. Avoid prolonged heating of the slide as it can shatter from excessive exposure to heat. The underside of the slide should feel warm to the touch.

Laboratory Report

Answer the questions on Laboratory Report 10–13 that relate to this exercise.

read

Gram Staining

exercise

14

In 1884, the Danish physician Christian Gram was trying to develop a staining procedure that would differentiate bacterial cells from eukaryotic nuclei in stained tissue samples. Although Gram was not completely successful in developing a tissue stain, what resulted from his work is the most important stain in bacteriology, the Gram stain. The Gram stain is an example of a differential stain. These staining reactions take advantage of the fact that cells or structures within cells display dissimilar staining reactions that can be distinguished by the use of different dyes. In the Gram stain, the two kinds of cells, gram-positive and gram-negative, can be identified by their respective colors, purple and red to pink after performing the staining method. The procedure is based on the fact that gram-positive bacteria retain a crystal violet-iodine complex through decolorization with alcohol or acetone. Gram-positive bacteria appear as purple when viewed by microscopy. In contrast, alcohol or acetone removes the crystal violet-iodine complex from gram-negative bacteria. These bacteria must, therefore, be counterstained with a red dye, safranin, after the decolorization step in order to be visualized by microscopy. Hence, gram-negative bacteria appear as pink to red cells when viewed by microscopy.

Figure 14.1 illustrates the appearance of cells after each step in the Gram-stain procedure. Note that initially both gram-positive and gram-negative cells are stained by the **primary stain,** crystal violet. In the second step of the procedure, Gram's iodine is added to the smear. Iodine is a **mordant** that complexes with the crystal violet and forms an insoluble complex in gram-positive cells. At this point, both types of cells will still appear

Reagent	Gram positive	Gram negative
None (Heat-fixed cells)		
Crystal Violet (20 seconds)		
Gram's Iodine (1 minute)		
Ethyl Alcohol (10–20 seconds)		
Safranin (1 minute)		

Figure 14.1   Color changes that occur at each step in the Gram-staining process.

as purple. The dye-mordant complex is not removed from gram-positive bacteria but is leached from gram-negative cells by the alcohol or acetone in the **decolorization** step. After decolorization, gram-positive cells are purple but gram-negative cells are colorless. In the final step, a **counterstain,** safranin, is applied, which stains the colorless gram-negative cells. The appearance of the gram-positive cells is unchanged because the crystal violet is a much more intense stain than safranin.

The mechanism for how the Gram stain works is related to chemical differences in the cell walls of gram-positive and gram-negative bacteria (figure 14.2). When viewed by electron microscopy, gram-positive cells have a thick layer of **peptidoglycan** that comprises the

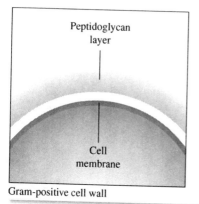

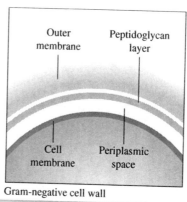

Figure 14.2   Comparison of gram-positive and gram-negative cell walls.

Gram-positive cell wall

Gram-negative cell wall

**Microbiology, 11th Edition,
Short Version**

EXERCISE 14 ┃ Gram Staining

cell wall of these organisms. In contrast, the cell wall in gram-negative cells consists of an outer membrane that covers a much thinner layer of peptidoglycan. It is these significant differences in structure that probably determines whether the dye-mordant complex is removed from the gram-negative cell or remains associated with the gram-positive cell.

Of all the staining techniques you will use in microbiology, the Gram stain is one of the most important. It will be critical in identifying your unknown bacteria and you will use it routinely in many exercises in this manual. Although this technique seems quite simple, performing it with a high degree of reliability requires some practice and experience. Several factors can affect the outcome of the procedure:

1. It is important to use cultures that are 16–18 hours old. Gram-positive cultures older than this can convert to gram-variable or gram-negative and give erroneous results. (It is important to note that gram-negative bacteria never convert to gram-positive.)
2. It is critical to prepare thin smears. Thin smears allow the observation of individual cells and any arrangement in which the cells occur. Furthermore, the thickness of your smears can affect

decolorization. Thick smears can entrap the primary stain, which is not removed by alcohol or acetone. Cells that occur in the entrapped stain can appear gram-positive leading to erroneous results.
3. Decolorization is the most critical step in the Gram-stain procedure. If the destaining reagent is over-applied, the dye-mordant complex can eventually be removed from gram-positive cells, converting them to gram-negative cells.

During this laboratory period, you will be provided an opportunity to stain several different kinds of bacteria to see if you can achieve the degree of success that is required. Remember, if you don't master this technique now, you will have difficulty with your unknowns later.

Staining Procedure

Materials

- slides with heat-fixed smears
- Gram-staining kit and wash bottle
- bibulous paper

1. Cover the smear with **crystal violet** and let stand for *20 seconds* (see figure 14.3).

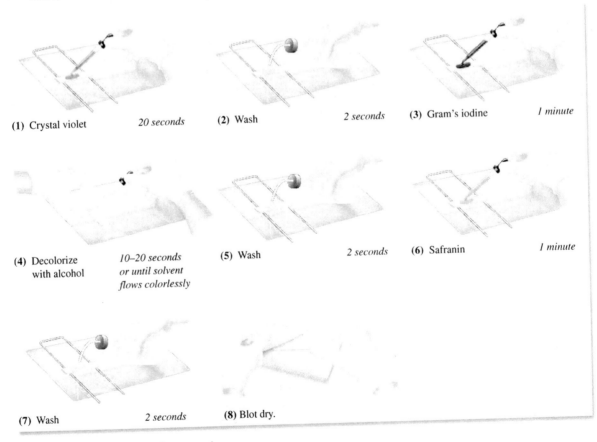

(1) Crystal violet   *20 seconds*   (2) Wash   *2 seconds*   (3) Gram's iodine   *1 minute*

(4) Decolorize with alcohol   *10–20 seconds or until solvent flows colorlessly*   (5) Wash   *2 seconds*   (6) Safranin   *1 minute*

(7) Wash   *2 seconds*   (8) Blot dry.

Figure 14.3 The Gram-staining procedure.

**Microbiology, 11th Edition,
Short Version**

2. Briefly wash off the stain, using a wash bottle of distilled water. Drain off excess water.
3. Cover the smear with **Gram's iodine** solution and let it stand for *one minute*. (Your instructor may prefer only 30 seconds for this step.)
4. Wash off the Gram's iodine. Hold the slide at a 45-degree angle and allow the 95% alcohol to flow down the surface of the slide. Do this until the alcohol is colorless as it flows from the smear down the surface of the slide. *This should take no more than 20 seconds for properly prepared smears.* Note: thick smears can take longer than 20 seconds for decolorization.
5. Stop decolorization by washing the slide with a gentle stream of water.
6. Cover the smear with **safranin** for 1 minute.
7. Wash gently for a few seconds, blot dry with bibulous paper, and air-dry.
8. Examine the slide under oil immersion.

Assignments

The organisms that will be used here for Gram staining represent a diversity of form and staining characteristics. Some of the rods and cocci are gram-positive; others are gram-negative. One rod-shaped organism is a spore-former and another is acid-fast. The challenge here is to make Gram-stained slides of various combinations that reveal their differences.

Materials

* broth cultures of *Staphylococcus aureus,* *Pseudomonas aeruginosa,* and *Moraxella (Branhamella) catarrhalis*
* nutrient agar slant cultures of *Bacillus megaterium* and *Mycobacterium smegmatis*

Mixed Organisms I   (Triple Smear Practice Slides) Prepare three slides with three smears on each slide. On the left portion of each slide make a smear of *Staphylococcus aureus.* On the right portion of each slide make a smear of *Pseudomonas aeruginosa.* In the middle of the slide make a smear that is a mixture of both organisms, using two loopfuls of each organism. *Be sure to flame the loop sufficiently to avoid contaminating cultures.*

Gram stain one slide first, saving the other two for later. Examine the center smear. If done properly, you should see purple cocci and pink to red rods as shown in illustration 3, figure 14.4.

Call your instructor over to evaluate your slide. If the slide is improperly stained, the instructor will be able to tell what went wrong by examining all three smears. He or she will inform you how to correct your technique when you stain the next triple smear reserve slide.

Record your results on Laboratory Report 14–16 by drawing a few cells in the appropriate circle.

Mixed Organisms II   Make a Gram-stained slide of a mixture of *Bacillus megaterium* and *Moraxella (Branhamella) catarrhalis.*

This mixture differs from the previous slide in that the rods (*B. megaterium*) will be purple and the cocci (*M.B. catarrhalis*) will be large pink to red diplococci. See illustration 4, figure 14.4.

As you examine this slide, look for clear areas in the rods, which represent endospores. Since endospores are refractile and impermeable to crystal violet, they will appear as transparent holes in the cells.

Draw a few cells in the appropriate circle on your Laboratory Report sheet.

Acid-Fast Bacteria   To see how acid-fast mycobacteria react to Gram's stain, make a Gram-stained slide of *Mycobacterium smegmatis.* If your staining technique is correct, the organisms should appear gram-positive.

Draw a few cells in the appropriate circle on your Laboratory Report sheet.

**Microbiology, 11th Edition,
Short Version**

EXERCISE 14 ▌ Gram Staining

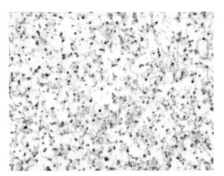

(1) Simple stain
Bacillus subtilis and Staphylococcus

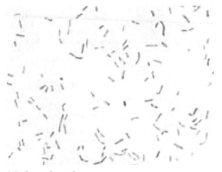

(2) Capsule stain
Klebsiella pneumoniae

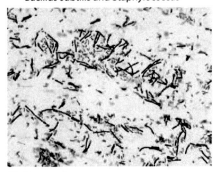

(3) Gram stain
Bacillus megaterium and Escherichia

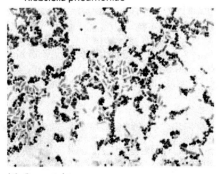

(4) Gram stain
Escherichia coli and Staphylococcus aureus

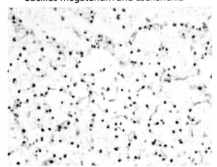

(5) Endospore stain
Clostridium sporogenes

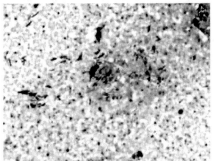

(6) Acid-fast stain
Mycobacterium smegmatis and
Staphylococcus aureus

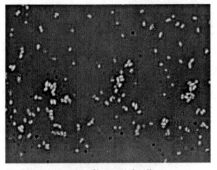

(7) Negative stain of bacterial cells

Figure 14.4   Photomicrographs of representative stains (630X).
© The McGraw-Hill Companies, Inc./Auburn University Research Instrumentation Facility/Michael Miller, photographer.

Spore Staining:
Two Methods

(read)

15

When species of bacteria belonging to the genera *Bacillus* and *Clostridia* exhaust essential nutrients, they undergo a complex developmental cycle that produces resting stages called **endospores.** Endospores allow these bacteria to survive environmental conditions that are not favorable for growth. If nutrients once again become available, the endospore can go through the process of germination to form a new vegetative cell and growth will resume. Endospores are very dehydrated structures that are not actively metabolizing. Furthermore, they are resistant to heat, radiation, acids, and many chemicals, such as disinfectants, that normally harm or kill vegetative cells. Their resistance is due in part to the fact that they have a protein coat, or **exosporium,** that forms a protective barrier around the spore. Heat resistance is associated with the water content of endospores. The higher the water content of an endospore, the less heat resistant the endospore will be. During sporulation, the water content of the endospore is reduced to 10–30% of the vegetative cell. This results because calcium ions complex with spore-specific proteins and a chemical, dipicolinic acid. The latter compound is not found in vegetative cells. This complex forms a gel that controls the amount of water that can enter the endospore, thus maintaining its dehydrated state.

Since endospores are not easily destroyed by heat or chemicals, they define the conditions necessary to establish sterility. For example, to destroy endospores by heating, they must be exposed for 15 to 20 minutes to steam under pressure, which generates temperatures of 121° C. Such conditions are produced in an **autoclave.**

The resistant properties of endospores also mean that they are not easily penetrated by stains. For example in Exercise 14, you observed that endospores did not readily Gram stain. If endospore-containing cells are stained by basic stains such as crystal violet, the spores appear as unstained areas in the vegetative cell.

However, if heat is applied while staining with malachite green, the stain penetrates the endospore and becomes entrapped in the endospore. The malachite green is not removed by subsequent washing with decolorizing agents or water. In this instance, heat is acting as mordant to facilitate the uptake of the stain.

Schaeffer-Fulton Method

The Schaeffer-Fulton method, which is depicted in figure 15.1, utilizes malachite green to stain the endospore and safranin to stain the vegetative portion of the cell. Utilizing this technique, a properly stained spore-former will have a green endospore contained in a pink sporangium. Illustration 5, figure 14.4, on page 104 reveals what such a slide looks like under oil immersion.

Prepare a smear of *Bacillus megaterium* and allow the smear to air-dry. Heat fix the dried smear and follow the steps for staining outlined in figure 15.1.

Materials

- 24–36 hour nutrient agar slant culture of *Bacillus megaterium*
- electric hot plate and small beaker (25 ml)
- spore-staining kit consisting of a bottle each of 5% malachite green and safranin

Dorner Method

The Dorner method for staining endospores produces a red spore within a colorless sporangium. Nigrosin is used to provide a dark background for contrast. The six steps involved in this technique are shown in figure 15.2. Although both the sporangium and endospore are stained during boiling in step 3, the sporangium is decolorized by the diffusion of safranin molecules into the nigrosin.

Prepare a slide of *Bacillus megaterium* that utilizes the Dorner method. Follow the steps in figure 15.2.

**Microbiology, 11th Edition,
Short Version**

EXERCISE 15 ▌ Spore Staining

(1) Cover smear with small piece of paper toweling and saturate it with malachite green. Steam over boiling water for *5 minutes*. Add additional stain if stain boils off.

(2) After the slide has cooled sufficiently, remove the paper toweling and rinse with water for 30 seconds.

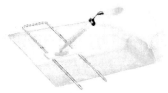

(3) Counterstain with safranin for about *20 seconds*.

(4) Rinse briefly with water to remove safranin.

(5) Blot dry with bibulous paper, and examine slide under oil immersion.

Figure 15.1   The Schaeffer-Fulton spore stain method.

Materials

- nigrosin
- electric hot plate and small beaker (25 ml)
- small test tube (10 × 75 mm size)
- test-tube holder
- 24–36 hour nutrient agar slant culture of *Bacillus megaterium*

Quick Spore Stain

A variation on the Schaeffer-Fulton method is a quick method that uses the same stains.

Materials

- *Bacillus megaterium* slant cultures, older than 36 hours
- malachite green stain
- safranin stain
- staining racks
- clothespins

Procedure

1. Prepare a smear of the organism and allow it to air-dry.
2. Grasp the slide with the air-dried smear with a clothespin and pass it through a Bunsen burner flame 10 times. Be careful not to overdo the heating as the slide can break.
3. Immediately flood the smear with malachite green and allow to stand for 5 minutes.
4. Wash the smear with a gentle stream of water.
5. Stain with safranin for 45 seconds. Spores will be green and the vegetative cell will be red.

Laboratory Report

After examining the organisms under oil immersion, draw a few cells in the appropriate circles in Laboratory Report 14–16.

Spore Staining   ▌   EXERCISE 15

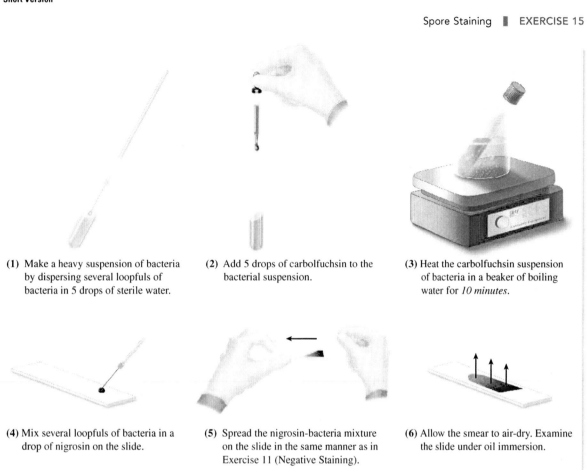

(1) Make a heavy suspension of bacteria by dispersing several loopfuls of bacteria in 5 drops of sterile water.

(2) Add 5 drops of carbolfuchsin to the bacterial suspension.

(3) Heat the carbolfuchsin suspension of bacteria in a beaker of boiling water for *10 minutes*.

(4) Mix several loopfuls of bacteria in a drop of nigrosin on the slide.

(5) Spread the nigrosin-bacteria mixture on the slide in the same manner as in Exercise 11 (Negative Staining).

(6) Allow the smear to air-dry. Examine the slide under oil immersion.

Figure 15.2   **The Dorner spore stain method.**

read

Acid-Fast Staining:
Ziehl-Neelsen Method

16

exercise

Bacteria such as *Mycobacterium* and some *Nocardia* have cell walls that contain a high lipid content. One of the cell wall lipids is a waxy material called **mycolic acid.** This material is a complex lipid that is composed of fatty acids and fatty alcohols that have hydrocarbon chains up to 80 carbons in length. It significantly affects the staining properties of these bacteria and prevents them from being stained by many of the stains routinely used in microbiology. The acid-fast stain is an important diagnostic tool in the identification of *Mycobacterium tuberculosis* the causative agent of tuberculosis, and *Mycobacterium leprae* the bacterium that causes leprosy in humans.

To facilitate staining of these bacteria, it is necessary to use techniques that make the cells more permeable to stains. In the classic Ziehl-Neelsen staining method, the primary stain, carbolfuchsin, is mixed with phenol and the cells are heated for 5 minutes during the staining procedure. Phenol is necessary for the carbofuchsin to penetrate the waxy cell wall lipids and heating further facilitates the penetration of the stain. Heat acts as a mordant to make the stain complex more permeable to the mycolic acid. Subsequent treatment of the cells with acid-alcohol, a decolorizer, does not remove the entrapped stain. Hence, these cells are termed **acid-fast.** Cells that do not contain mycolic acid in their cell walls are easily decolorized by acid-alcohol and are termed **non-acid-fast.** To be visualized, non-acid-fast bacteria must be counterstained with methylene blue. In the acid-fast staining method, acid-fast cells appear red to pink in stained preparations, whereas non-acid-fast cells appear blue (figure 14.4, photo 6). The application of heat to cells during staining with carbolfuchsin and phenol is not without concerns. Phenol can vaporize when heated, giving rise to noxious fumes that are toxic to the eyes and mucous membranes. The Kinyoun acid-fast method is a modification in which the concentrations of both carbolfuchsin and phenol are increased but the bacterial cells are not heated during the staining procedure. The increased concentrations of the stain

and phenol are sufficient to allow penetration of stain into cells and the carbolfuchsin is not removed by destaining with acid-alcohol. This procedure has the further advantage that phenol fumes are not generated during the staining of the cells.

In the following exercise, you will prepare an acid-fast stain of a mixture of *Mycobacterium smegmatis* and *Staphylococcus aureus* using the Kinyoun method for acid-fast staining. *M. smegmatis* is a nonpathogenic, acid-fast rod that occurs in soil and on the external genitalia of humans. *S. aureus* is a non-acid-fast coccus that is also part of the normal flora of humans but that can also be a serious opportunistic pathogen.

Materials

- nutrient agar slant culture of *Mycobacterium smegmatis* (48-hour culture)
- nutrient broth culture of *S. aureus*
- electric hot plate and small beaker
- acid-fast staining kit (carbolfuchsin, acid-alcohol, and methylene blue)

Smear Preparation   Prepare a mixed culture smear by placing two loopfuls of *S. aureus* on a slide and transferring a small amount of *M. smegmatis* to the broth on the slide with an inoculating needle. Since the Mycobacteria are waxy and tend to cling to each other in clumps, break up the masses of organisms with the inoculating needle. After air-drying the smear, heat-fix it.

Staining   Follow the staining procedure outlined in figure 16.1.

Examination   Examine under oil immersion and compare your slide with illustration 6, figure 14.4 on page 104.

Laboratory Report   Record your results in Laboratory Report 14–16.

**Microbiology, 11th Edition,
Short Version**

EXERCISE 16 ▮ Acid-Fast Staining

(1) Cover the heat–fixed smear with carbolfuchsin and stain for *5 minutes*.

(2) Wash with water and shake off any excess water.

(3) Decolorize with acid–alcohol for approxiamtely *1 minute*. Check by tilting the slide and adding more destain to make sure that no more stain runs off of the smear.

(4) Stop decolorization by the acid–alcohol by rinsing *briefly* with water.

(5) Counterstain with methylene blue for *30 seconds*.

(6) Rinse briefly with water to remove excess methylene blue.

(7) Blot dry with bibulous paper. Examine under oil immersion.

Figure 16.1   Kinyoun acid-fast staining procedure.

Motility Determination

17

The major organelles of motility in bacteria are **flagella.** Flagella allow cells to move toward nutrients in the environment or move away from harmful substances, such as acids, in a complicated process called **chemotaxis.** The flagellum is a rigid helical structure that extends as much as 10 microns out from the cell. However, flagella are very thin structures, less than 0.2 microns, and, therefore, they are below the resolution of the light microscope. For flagella to be observed by light microscopy, they must be stained by special techniques. An individual bacterial flagellum is composed of a rigid filament that occurs in the form of a helix. This constitutes the main body of the flagellum structure. The filament is connected to a hook that is attached to a shaft that is inserted into a series of rings whose number differ for gram-positive and gram-negative cells (figure 17.1). Gram-positive cells contain the S and M rings that are situated in the area of the cell membrane. Gram-negative cells also possess the S and M rings and two additional rings, the L and P rings that are associated with the outer membrane and

peptidoglycan of the cell. The shaft, rings, and accessory proteins make up the basal body of the flagellum. The basal body is situated in the cell membrane/cell wall area of the bacterial cell. Rotation of the flagellum is powered by a proton motive force (pmf) that is established when proteins associated with the basal body transport protons across the cell membrane, creating a charge differential across the membrane. The pmf induces the S and M rings to rotate which results in the rotation of the shaft, hook, and filament. Other proteins in the basal body can reverse the direction of rotation of the flagellum. The movement of the rigid and helical filament is analogous to the rotation of a propeller on a boat engine. Hence, the movement of the filament propels the bacterial cell in much the same way that a boat is moved through the water by its engine and propeller. This is in contrast to a eukaryotic flagellum, which causes the cell to move because the flagellum beats like a whip.

Motility and the arrangement of flagella around the cell (figure 17.2) are important taxonomic characteristics that are useful in characterizing bacteria.

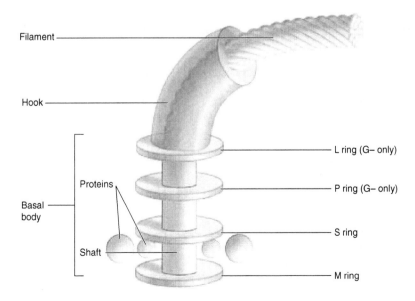

Figure 17.1   Structure of the Gram-negative bacterial flagellum

Microbiology, 11th Edition,
Short Version

EXERCISE 17 | Motility Determination

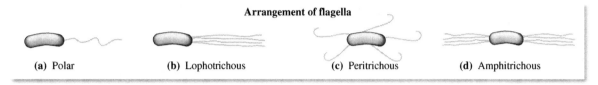

Figure 17.2   Arrangement of flagella

Motility can be determined by several methods. It can be determined microscopically by observing cells in a **wet mount.** In this procedure, a drop of viable cells is placed on a microscope slide and covered with a cover glass. The slide is then observed with a phase-contrast microscope. The rapid swimming movement of cells in the microscopic field confirms motility. However, wet mounts can easily dry out by evaporation, which is especially troublesome if observations need to made for prolonged periods of time. Drying can be delayed by using the **hanging drop technique,** shown in figure 17.3. In this procedure, a drop of cells is placed on a cover glass, which is then placed over a special slide that has a concave depression in its center. The coverslip is held in place with petroleum jelly, thus forming an enclosed glass chamber that prevents drying.

For the beginner, true swimming motility under the microscope must be differentiated from **Brownian motion** of cells or movement caused by currents under the cover glass. Brownian motion is movement due to molecular bombardment of cells causing cells to shake or "jiggle about" but not move in any vectorial way. Cells can also appear to move because currents can be created under the cover glass when pressure is exerted by focusing the oil immersion lens or by the wet mount drying out. This causes cells to "sweep" across the field.

Another method for determining motility involves inoculating semisoft agar medium. This medium has an agar concentration of 0.4%, which does not inhibit bacteria from "swimming" through the medium. In this procedure, the organisms are inoculated by stabbing the semisolid medium with an inoculating needle. If the organisms are motile, they will swim away from the line of inoculation into the uninoculated surrounding medium, causing the medium to be turbid. Non-motile bacteria will be found only along the line of inoculation. For pathogenic bacteria, such as the typhoid bacillus, the use of semisoft agar medium to determine motility is often preferred over microscope techniques because of the potential for infection posed by pathogens in making wet mounts.

In the following exercise, you will use both microscopic and culture media procedures to determine motility of bacterial cultures.

First Period

During the first period, you will make wet mounts and hanging drop slides of two organisms: *Proteus vulgaris* and *Micrococcus luteus.* Tube media (semisolid medium or SIM medium) and a soft agar plate will also be inoculated. The media inoculations will have to be incubated to be studied in the next period. Proceed as follows:

Materials

- microscope slides and cover glasses
- depression slide
- 2 tubes of semisolid or SIM medium
- 1 petri plate of soft nutrient agar (20–25 ml of soft agar per plate)
- nutrient broth cultures of *Micrococcus luteus* and *Proteus vulgaris* (young cultures)
- inoculating loop and needle
- Bunsen burner

Wet Mounts   Prepare wet mount slides of each of the organisms, using several loopfuls of the organism on the slides. Examine under an oil immersion objective. Observe the following guidelines:

- Use only scratch-free, clean slides and cover glasses. This is particularly important when using phase-contrast optics.
- Label each slide with the name of the organism.
- By manipulating the diaphragm and voltage control, reduce the lighting sufficiently to make the organisms visible. Unstained bacteria are very transparent and difficult to see.
- For proof of true motility, look for directional movement that is several times the long dimension of the bacterium. The movement will also occur in different directions in the same field.
- Ignore Brownian movement. *Brownian movement* is vibrational movement caused by invisible molecules bombarding bacterial cells. If the only movement you see is vibrational and not directional, the organism is non-motile.
- If you see only a few cells exhibiting motility, consider the organism to be motile. Characteristically, only a few of the cells will be motile at a given moment.

Motility Determination ▌ EXERCISE 17

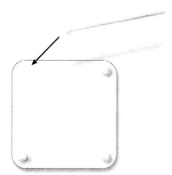

(1) A small amount of Vaseline is placed near each corner of the cover glass with a toothpick.

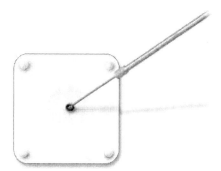

(2) Two loopfuls of organisms are placed in the cover glass.

(3) Depression slide is pressed against Vaseline on cover glass and quickly inverted.

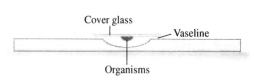

(4) The completed preparation can be examined under oil immersion.

Figure 17.3   The hanging drop slide.

- Don't confuse water current movements with true motility. Water currents are due to capillary action caused by temperature changes and drying out. All objects move in a straight line in one direction.
- And, finally, always *examine a wet mount immediately,* once it has been prepared, because motility decreases with time after preparation.

Hanging Drop Slides   By referring to figure 17.3, prepare hanging drop slides of each organism. Be sure to use clean cover glasses and label each slide with a china marking pencil. When placing loopfuls of organisms on the cover glass, be sure to flame the loop between applications. Once the slide is placed on the microscope stage, do as follows:

1. Examine the slide first with the low-power objective. If your microscope is equipped with an automatic stop, avoid using the stop; instead, use the coarse adjustment knob for bringing the image into focus. The greater thickness of the depression slide prevents one from being able to focus at the stop point.
2. Once the image is visible under low power, swing the high-dry objective into position and readjust the lighting. Since most bacteria are drawn to the

edge of the drop by surface tension, **focus near the edge of the drop.**
3. If your microscope has phase-contrast optics, switch to high-dry phase. Although a hanging drop does not provide the shallow field desired for phase-contrast, you may find that it works fairly well.
4. If you wish to use oil immersion, simply rotate the high-dry objective out of position, add immersion oil to the cover glass, and swing the oil immersion lens into position.
5. Avoid delay in using this setup. Water condensation may develop to decrease clarity and the organisms become less motile with time.
6. Review all the characteristics of bacterial motility that are stated on page 116 under wet mounts.

Tube Method   Inoculate tubes of semisolid or SIM media with each organism according to the following instructions:

1. Label the tubes of semisolid (or SIM) media with the names of the organisms. Place your initials on the tubes also.
2. Flame and cool the inoculating needle, and insert it into the culture after flaming the neck of the tube.

Microbiology, 11th Edition,
Short Version

EXERCISE 17 ▮ Motility Determination

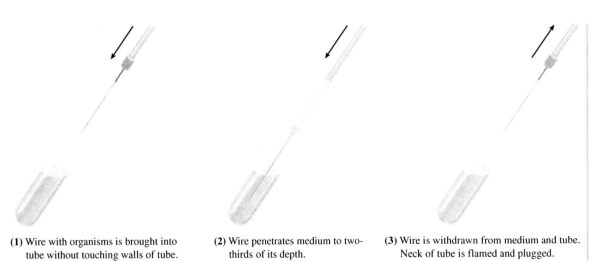

(1) Wire with organisms is brought into tube without touching walls of tube.

(2) Wire penetrates medium to two-thirds of its depth.

(3) Wire is withdrawn from medium and tube. Neck of tube is flamed and plugged.

Figure 17.4 Stab technique for motility test.

3. Remove the cap from the tube of medium, flame the neck, and stab it two-thirds of the way down to the bottom, as shown in figure 17.4. Flame the neck of the tube again before returning the cap to the tube.
4. Repeat steps 2 and 3 for the other culture.
5. Incubate the tubes at room temperature for 24 to 48 hours.

Plate Method   Mark the bottom of a plate of soft agar with two one-half inch circles about one inch apart. Label one circle ML and the other PV. These circles will be targets for your culture stabs. Put your initials on the plate also.

Using proper aseptic techniques, stab the medium in the center of the ML circle with *M. luteus* and the center of the other circle with *P. vulgaris*. Incubate the plate for 24 to 48 hours at room temperature.

Second Period

Assemble the following materials that were inoculated during the last period and incubated.

Materials

• culture tubes of motility medium that have been incubated
• inoculated petri plate that has been incubated

Compare the two tubes that were inoculated with *M. luteus* and *P. vulgaris*. Look for cloudiness as evidence of motility. *Proteus* should exhibit motility. Does it? Record your results on the Laboratory Report.

Compare the appearance of the two stabs in the soft agar. Describe the differences that exist in the two stabs.

Does the plate method provide any better differentiation of results than the tube method?

Laboratory Report

Complete the Laboratory Report for this exercise.

17

Laboratory Report

Student: _____

Date: _____ Section: _____

17 Motility Determination

A. Results

1. Which bacterial species exhibited true motility on the slides?

   _____

   _____

2. Draw the appearance of the inoculated SIM tubes. Did the semisolid medium inoculations concur with the slide results?

   _____

   _____

   Micrococcus luteus   *Proteus vulgaris*

B. Short Answer Questions

1. Describe the structure of a flagellum. How do flagella generate cell motility?

   _____

   _____

2. If you compared two motile bacterial species and determined one was considerably more motile than the other, which arrangement of flagella would you expect to be associated with the highly motile species? How would you confirm this supposition?

   _____

   _____

3. Differentiate between the following types of movement observed in a wet mount or hanging drop slide.

   a. true motility.

   _____

   b. Brownian movement.

   _____

   c. water current movement.

   _____

Microbiology, 11th Edition,
Short Version

Motility Determination (continued)

4. Between wet mount and hanging drop slide preparations, which is more resistant to evaporation? Which works best with phase-contrast microscopy?

5. What concentration of agar is used in a semisolid medium for motility determination? How does that compare to a typical solid medium (*see Exercise 18*)? Explain.

6. Why are semisolid media sometimes preferred over slide techniques for evaluating bacterial motility?

7. If SIM medium was used for motility determination for *Proteus vulgaris,* what noticeable change to the medium was observed? (*Hint: see Exercise 40 to find out what the letters "SIM" represent.*)

Identification of Unknown Bacteria

PART

8

One of the most interesting experiences in introductory microbiology is to attempt to identify an unknown microorganism that has been assigned to you as a laboratory problem. The next six exercises pertain to this phase of microbiological work. You will be given one or more cultures of bacteria to identify. The only information that might be given to you about your unknowns will pertain to their sources and habitats. All the information needed for identification will have to be acquired by you through independent study.

Although you will be engrossed in trying to identify an unknown organism, there is a more fundamental underlying objective of this series of exercises that goes far beyond simply identifying an unknown. That objective is to gain an understanding of the cultural and physiological characteristics of bacteria. Physiological characteristics will be determined with a series of biochemical tests that you will perform on the organisms. Although correctly identifying the unknowns that are given to you is very important, it is just as important that you thoroughly understand the chemistry of the tests that you perform on the organisms.

The first step in the identification procedure is to accumulate information that pertains to the organisms' morphological, cultural, and physiological (biochemical) characteristics. This involves making different kinds of slides for cellular studies and the inoculation of various types of media to note the growth characteristics and types of enzymes produced. As this information is accumulated, it is recorded in an orderly manner on descriptive charts, which are located in the back of the manual.

After sufficient information has been recorded, the next step is to consult a taxonomic key, which enables one to identify the organism. For this final step, *Bergey's Manual of Systematic Bacteriology* will be used. Copies of volumes 1 and 2 of this book will be available in the laboratory, library, or both.

Success in this endeavor will require meticulous techniques, intelligent interpretation, and careful record keeping. Your mastery of aseptic methods in the handling of cultures and the performance of inoculations will show up clearly in your results. Contamination of your cultures with unwanted organisms will yield false results, making identification hazardous speculation. If you have reason to doubt the validity of the results of a specific test, repeat it; *don't rely on chance!* As soon as you have made an observation or completed a test, record the information on the descriptive chart. Do not trust your memory—record data immediately.

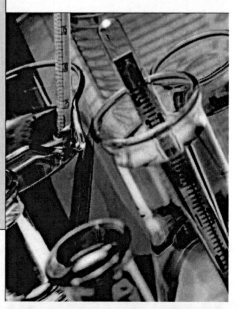

Morphological Study of Unknown Bacterium

The first step in the study of your unknown bacterium is to set up stock cultures that will be used in the subsequent exercises. A reserve stock culture will not be used for making slides or inoculating tests. It will be stored in the refrigerator in case your working stock becomes contaminated and you need to make a fresh working stock. The working stock will be used to inoculate the various tests that you will perform to identify your unknown bacterium. It is crucial that you practice good aseptic technique when inoculating from your working stock in order to avoid contaminating the culture. If it becomes contaminated or loses viability, you can prepare a fresh culture from the reserve stock culture that you have maintained in the refrigerator.

Identifying your unknown will be a kind of "microbiological adventure" that will test the skills and knowledge that you have acquired thus far. You will gather a great deal of information regarding your unknown by performing staining reactions and numerous metabolic tests. The Gram stain will play a very critical role in the process because it will eliminate thousands of possible organisms. The results of these tests will be compared to flow charts provided in this manual and to information in *Bergey's Manual.* From your "detective" work, you will be able to ascertain the identity of the unknown that you were given. To set up the stock cultures, proceed in the following way (see figure 36.1).

Stock Cultures

You will receive a broth culture or an agar slant of your unknown bacterium. From this culture you will prepare your working stock and your reserve stock cultures. From the working stock, you will be able to determine such things as cell morphology, the Gram reaction of the unknown, and, in some cases, whether the culture forms any pigment. You can also determine other morphological characteristics such as the presence of a glycocalyx, endospores, or cytoplasmic granules.

Materials

First Period

* nutrient agar or tryptone agar slants

1. Label the agar slants with the code number of the unknown, your name, lab section, and date.
2. Inoculate both slants with your unknown organism. Begin your streak at the bottom of the slant and move the inoculating loop toward the top of the slant in a straight motion. Remember to practice good aseptic technique.
3. Place the respective tubes in the appropriate baskets labeled with the two incubation temperatures, 20° C and 37° C (figure 36.1). Incubate the slants for 18–24 hours.

Second Period

1. Examine the slants. Look for growth. Some organisms produce sparse growth and you must examine the cultures closely to determine if growth is present. Is either culture producing a pigment and, if so, is the pigment associated with the cells or has it diffused into the agar? Remember, however, that pigment production could require longer incubation times.
2. Determine which incubation temperature produced the best growth. If no growth occurred on either slant, your original culture could be nonviable or more time is needed for growth of the culture to occur. A third possibility is that neither temperature supported growth. Think through the possibilities and decide what course of action you need to take.
3. If growth occurred on the slant, pick the tube with the best growth and designate it as your **reserve stock culture.** Store the reserve stock in the refrigerator. Cultures stored in this manner are viable for several weeks. Do not use the reserve stock to make inoculations of the various media you will employ or to make stains. **Do not store the culture in your desk.**

Microbiology, 11th Edition,
Short Version

EXERCISE 36 | Morphological Study of Unknown Bacterium

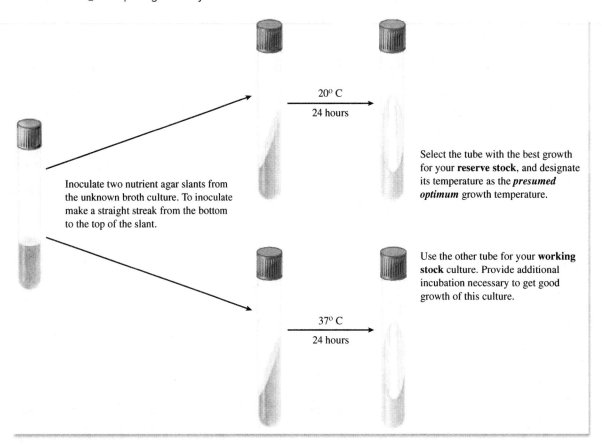

Inoculate two nutrient agar slants from the unknown broth culture. To inoculate make a straight streak from the bottom to the top of the slant.

20° C
24 hours

37° C
24 hours

Select the tube with the best growth for your **reserve stock**, and designate its temperature as the *presumed optimum* growth temperature.

Use the other tube for your **working stock** culture. Provide additional incubation necessary to get good growth of this culture.

Figure 36.1   Stock culture procedure.

4. Designate the second culture as your **working stock culture.** This culture will be the source of the inoculum for the various tests and stains that you will perform (figure 36.2). If the culture is 18–24 hours old, it can be used to perform the Gram stain. If not, you will have to prepare a fresh slant from the working stock to do the Gram stain.

As soon as morphological information is acquired, be sure to record your observations on the descriptive chart on page 243. Proceed as follows:

Materials

- Gram-staining kit
- spore-staining kit
- acid-fast staining kit
- Loeffler's methylene blue stain
- nigrosin or india ink
- tubes of nutrient broth and nutrient agar
- gummed labels for test tubes

New Inoculations

For all of these staining techniques, you will need 24–48 hour cultures of your unknown. If your working stock slant is a fresh culture, use it. If you don't have a fresh broth culture of your unknown, inoculate a tube of nutrient broth and incubate it at its estimated optimum temperature for 24 hours.

Gram's Stain

Once you have a good Gram stain of your organism, you can determine several characteristics of your unknown. First, you should be able to determine the morphology of your organism: rod, coccus, spiral, etc. Furthermore, if you have prepared a thin smear, you can ascertain something about the arrangement of the cells. Note whether the cells occur singly, in pairs, in masses, or in chains. For example, the streptococci occur in chains whereas the staphylococci occur in masses much like a bunch of grapes. The Gram stain can also be used to determine the size of your organism. Refer to Exercise 4.

**Microbiology, 11th Edition,
Short Version**

Morphological Study of Unknown Bacterium ▮ EXERCISE 36

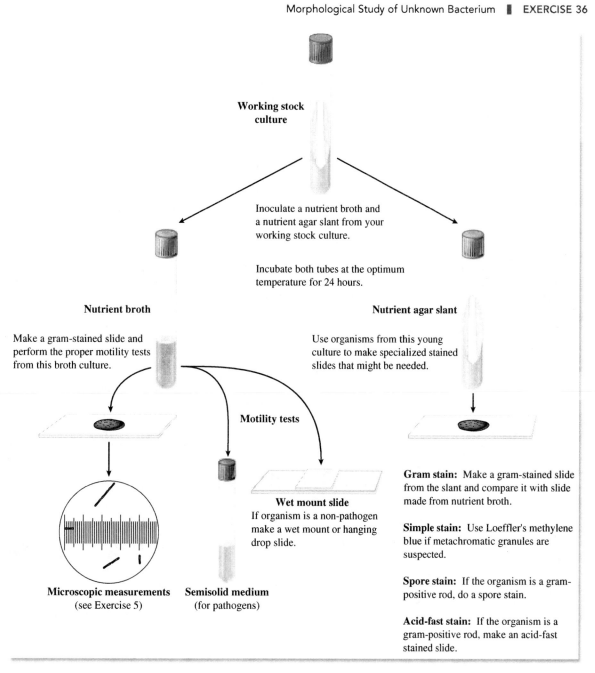

Figure 36.2   **Procedure for morphological study.**

Note: The results from the Gram stain can be verified by performing the following test. Place one drop of 3% KOH on a microscope slide and transfer a loopful of your unknown cells to the KOH solution. While observing the slide edge-on at eye level, mix the cells and KOH solution and slowly raise the loop from the cells. Gram-negative cells will lyse in the KOH solution, releasing their DNA and causing the liquid to become very viscous. Often, "strings" of DNA can be seen adhering to the loop as it is raised from the slide. Gram-positive cells do not undergo lysis in the KOH solution, and hence an increase in viscosity or DNA strings will not be seen in these cells.

Keep in mind that short rods with round ends (coccobacilli) look like cocci. If you have what seems to be a coccobacillus, examine many cells before

Microbiology, 11th Edition,
Short Version

EXERCISE 36 ▌ Morphological Study of Unknown Bacterium

you make a final decision. Also, keep in mind that *while rod-shaped organisms frequently appear as cocci under certain growth conditions, cocci rarely appear as rods.* (*Streptococcus mutans* is unique in forming rods under certain conditions.) Thus, it is generally safe to assume that if you have a slide on which you see both coccus-like cells and short rods, the organism is probably rod-shaped. This assumption is valid, however, only if you are not working with a contaminated culture!

Record the shape of the organism and its reaction to the stain on the descriptive chart on page 243.

Motility

For nonpathogens, the wet mount or hanging drop prepared from a broth culture is the preferred way to determine motility. Refer to Exercise 17. For pathogens, SIM medium can be used to ascertain motility (Exercise 17). Inoculate the culture by stabbing the "deep" with an inoculating needle. If growth occurs only along the line of inoculation, the organism is non-motile. In contrast, turbidity throughout the tube would indicate that your organism is motile. In general, cocci are non-motile whereas rods can be either motile or non-motile.

Endospores

If your unknown is a gram-positive rod, it may be an endospore former. Endospores, however, do not usually occur in cocci or in gram-negative rods. Examination of your gram-stained slide made from the agar slant should provide a clue since endospores show up as transparent oval structures in gram-stained preparations. Endospores can also be seen on unstained organisms if studied with phase-contrast optics.

If there seems to be evidence that the organism is a spore-former, make a slide using one of the spore-staining techniques you used in Exercise 15. *Since some spore-formers require at least a week's time of incubation before forming spores, it is prudent to double-check for spores in older cultures.*

Record on the descriptive chart whether the spore is terminal, subterminal, or in the middle of the rod.

Acid-Fast Staining

The mycobacteria and some species of *Nocardia* are acid-fast. For these bacteria, the presence of acid-fastness can interfere with the Gram stain, causing these bacteria to stain gram-negative. Performing the acid-fast stain will sort out part of this problem. Do not depend solely on the Gram stain as the results can be misleading, especially for the acid-fast bacteria.

If your unknown is a gram-positive, non-spore-forming rod, it could be an acid-fast bacterium. Acid-fastness can vary with culture age, but most cultures display this property after 2 days of incubation. For best results, do not do this stain on old cultures. Refer to Exercise 16 for the staining procedure.

Other Structures

If the cytoplasm in the gram-stained cells appears uneven, you may want to do a simple stain with Loeffler's methylene blue (Exercise 11) to determine the presence of metachromatic granules (volutin), which are storage granules of polyphosphate.

Although a capsule stain (Exercise 13) may be performed at this time, it might be better to wait until a later date when you have the organism growing on blood agar. Capsules usually are more apparent when the organisms are grown on this medium.

Laboratory Report

There is no Laboratory Report to fill out for this exercise. All information is recorded on the descriptive chart.

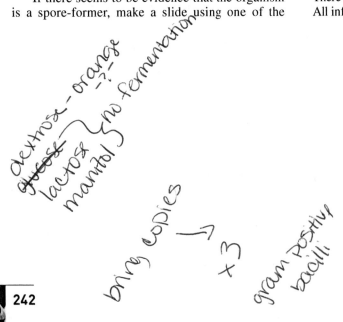

Cultural Characteristics

The cultural characteristics of an organism pertain to its macroscopic appearance on different kinds of media. In *Bergey's Manual,* you will find descriptive terms used by bacteriologists for recording cultural characteristics. For the general description of colonies, nutrient agar or any complex, rich medium is useful for this purpose. The nature of the growth in a nutrient broth can vary, and this too can be a source of certain information about an organism. Thioglycollate medium (Exercise 19) can be used to determine the oxygen requirements of an organism: Do the cells grow in a tube of this medium? Some media, such as blood agar are "differential," demonstrating the hemolytic capability of an organism. In the following exercise, you will inoculate your unknown into different media to determine its cultural characteristics in the various media.

First Period

(Inoculations)

During this period, one nutrient agar plate, one nutrient gelatin deep, two nutrient broths, and one tube of fluid thioglycollate medium will be inoculated. Inoculations will be made with the original broth culture of your unknown. The reason for inoculating two tubes of nutrient broth here is to recheck the optimum growth temperature of your unknown. In Exercise 36, you incubated your nutrient agar slants at 20° C and 37° C. It may well be that the optimum growth temperature is closer to 30° C. It is to check out this intermediate temperature that an extra nutrient broth is being inoculated. Proceed as follows:

Materials

for each unknown:
- 1 nutrient agar pour
- 1 nutrient gelatin deep
- 2 nutrient broths
- 1 fluid thioglycollate medium (FTM)
- 1 petri plate

1. Pour a petri plate of nutrient agar for each unknown and streak it with a method that will give good isolation of colonies. Use the original broth culture for streaking.
2. Inoculate the tubes of nutrient broth with a loop.

3. Make a stab inoculation into the gelatin deep by stabbing the inoculating needle (straight wire) directly down into the medium to the bottom of the tube and pulling it straight out. The medium must not be disturbed laterally.
4. Inoculate the tube of FTM with a loopful of your unknown. Mix the organisms throughout the tube by rolling the tube between your palms.
5. Place all tubes except one nutrient broth into a basket and incubate for 24 hours at the temperature that seemed optimal in Exercise 36. Incubate the remaining tube of nutrient broth separately at 30° C. Incubate the agar plate, inverted, at the presumed best temperature.

Second Period

(Evaluation)

After the cultures have been properly incubated, *carry them to your desk in a careful manner* to avoid disturbing the growth pattern in the nutrient broths and FTM. Before studying any of the tubes or plates, place the tube of nutrient gelatin in an ice water bath. It will be studied later. Proceed as follows to study each type of medium and record the proper descriptive terminology on the descriptive chart on page 243.

Materials

- reserve stock agar slant of unknown
- spectrophotometer and cuvettes
- hand lens
- ice water bath near sink

Nutrient Agar Slant (Reserve Stock)

Examine your reserve stock agar slant of your unknown that has been stored in the refrigerator since the last laboratory period. Evaluate it in terms of the following criteria:

Amount of Growth   The abundance of growth may be described as *none, slight, moderate,* and *abundant.*

Color   Pigments can be associated with a colony, for example, prodigiosin, the red pigment made by *Serratia marcescens* when grown at 27° C. However, pigments can be produced by an organism that diffuse

Microbiology, 11th Edition,
Short Version

EXERCISE 37 ▌ Cultural Characteristics

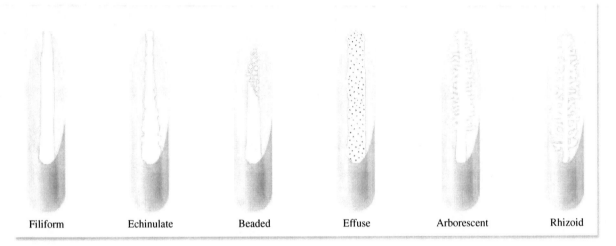

| Filiform | Echinulate | Beaded | Effuse | Arborescent | Rhizoid |

Figure 37.1 **Types of bacterial growth on nutrient agar slants.**

into the medium, causing the medium to be colored, such as the case for the green fluorescent pigment produced by *Pseudomonas fluorescens*. To check for diffusable pigments, hold your plate up to the light and observe the color of the medium in the plate. Most bacteria, however, do not produce pigments, and their colonies are white or buff colored.

Opacity   Organisms that grow prolifically on the surface of a medium will appear more opaque than those that exhibit a small amount of growth. Degrees of opacity may be expressed in terms of *opaque, transparent,* and *translucent* (partially transparent).

Form   The gross appearance of different types of growth are illustrated in figure 37.1. The following descriptions of each type will help in differentiation:

> *Filiform:* characterized by uniform growth along the line of inoculation
> *Echinulate:* margins of growth exhibit toothed appearance
> *Beaded:* separate or semiconfluent colonies along the line of inoculation
> *Effuse:* growth is thin, veil-like, unusually spreading
> *Arborescent:* branched, treelike growth
> *Rhizoid:* rootlike appearance

Nutrient Broth

The nature of growth on the surface, subsurface, and bottom of the tube is significant in nutrient broth cultures. Describe your cultures as thoroughly as possible on the descriptive chart with respect to these characteristics:

Surface   Figure 37.2 illustrates different types of surface growth. A *pellicle* type of surface differs from the *membranous* type in that the latter is much thinner. A *flocculent* surface is made up of floating adherent masses of bacteria.

Subsurface   Below the surface, the broth may be described as *turbid* if it is cloudy, *granular* if specific small particles can be seen, *flocculent* if small masses are floating around, and *flaky* if large particles are in suspension.

Sediment   The amount of sediment in the bottom of the tube may vary from none to a great deal. To describe the type of sediment, agitate the tube, putting the material in suspension. The type of sediment can be described as *granular, flocculent, flaky,* and *viscid*. Test for viscosity by probing the bottom of the tube with a sterile inoculating loop.

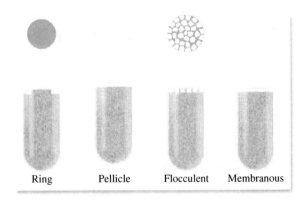

| Ring | Pellicle | Flocculent | Membranous |

Figure 37.2 **Types of surface growth in nutrient broth.**

Cultural Characteristics ▐ EXERCISE 37

Amount of Growth   To determine the amount of growth, it is necessary to shake the tube to disperse the organisms. Terms such as *slight* (scanty), *moderate*, and *abundant* adequately describe the amount.

Temperature Requirements   To determine which temperature produces better growth, transfer the contents of the nutrient broth tubes to separate cuvettes and measure the optical density (absorbance) with a spectrophotometer. Because the cultures may be too turbid to measure, you may have to dilute the cultures with water before taking the readings. Record in the descriptive chart which temperature produces better growth for your organism. This temperature will be closer to the one needed for optimum growth of your organism.

Fluid Thioglycollate Medium

The growth pattern of your bacterium in fluid thioglycollate medium will give some indication of the oxygen requirement of your organism. Examine your FTM tube and compare the growth pattern of your organism with that of figure 19.5 on page 136. More than likely, your bacterium will be either aerobic, microaerophilic, or a facultative anaerobe. Strict anaerobes such as *Clostridium* require special culture conditions for growth.

Gelatin Stab

Some bacteria produce **proteases,** enzymes that degrade proteins. Determine if your unknown produces proteases by examining the nutrient gelatin tube that you inoculated with your unknown. After incubation, place the culture in an ice bath and allow it to stand for several minutes. Remove the tube and tilt it several times from side to side to ascertain if liquefaction has occurred. Any degraded gelatin will remain liquid after being placed in the ice bath. If liquefaction has not occurred, the contents of the tube will be a solid. Also be sure to note if your organism can grow in gelatin since some bacteria are unable to do so. Check the configuration with figure 37.3 to see if any of the illustrations match your tube. A description of each type follows:

> *Crateriform:* saucer-shaped liquefaction
> *Napiform:* turnip-like
> *Infundibular:* funnel-like or inverted cone
> *Saccate:* elongate sac, tubular, cylindrical
> *Stratiform:* liquefied to the walls of the tube in the upper region

Note: The configuration of liquefaction is not as significant as the mere fact that liquefaction takes place. If your organism liquefies gelatin, but you are unable to

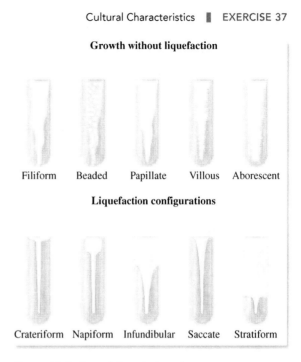

Growth without liquefaction

Filiform   Beaded   Papillate   Villous   Aborescent

Liquefaction configurations

Crateriform   Napiform   Infundibular   Saccate   Stratiform

Figure 37.3   Growth in gelatin stabs.

determine the exact configuration, don't worry about it. However, be sure to record on the descriptive chart the *presence* or *absence* of protease production.

Another important point: Some organisms produce protease at a very slow rate. Tubes that are negative should be incubated for another 4 or 5 days to see if protease is produced slowly.

Type of Growth   (No Liquefaction) If no liquefaction has occurred, check the tube to see if the organism grows in nutrient gelatin (some do, some don't). If growth has occurred, compare the growth with the top of the illustration in figure 37.3. It should be pointed out, however, that, from an identification standpoint, the nature of growth in gelatin is not very important.

Nutrient Agar Plate

Colonies grown on plates of nutrient agar should be studied with respect to size, color, opacity, form, elevation, and margin. With a dissecting microscope or hand lens study individual colonies carefully. Refer to figure 37.4 for descriptive terminology. Record your observations on the descriptive chart.

Laboratory Report

There is no Laboratory Report for this exercise. Record all information on the descriptive chart on page 243.

Microbiology, 11th Edition,
Short Version

EXERCISE 37 ▌ Cultural Characteristics

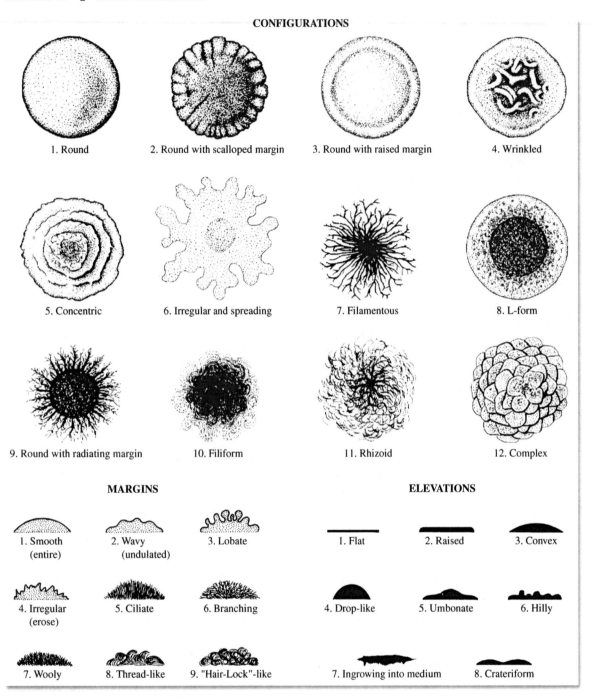

CONFIGURATIONS

1. Round

2. Round with scalloped margin

3. Round with raised margin

4. Wrinkled

5. Concentric

6. Irregular and spreading

7. Filamentous

8. L-form

9. Round with radiating margin

10. Filiform

11. Rhizoid

12. Complex

MARGINS

1. Smooth (entire)

2. Wavy (undulated)

3. Lobate

4. Irregular (erose)

5. Ciliate

6. Branching

7. Wooly

8. Thread-like

9. "Hair-Lock"-like

ELEVATIONS

1. Flat

2. Raised

3. Convex

4. Drop-like

5. Umbonate

6. Hilly

7. Ingrowing into medium

8. Crateriform

Figure 37.4   Colony characteristics.

Physiological Characteristics:
Oxidation and Fermentation Tests

38

The sum total of the chemical reactions that occur in a cell are referred to as metabolism, and the individual chemical reactions that make up the metabolic pathways in a cell are catalyzed by protein molecules called **enzymes.** Most enzymes function inside the cell where metabolic pathways carry out the breakdown (**catabolism**) of food materials and the biosynthesis of cell constituents (**anabolism**). Because bacteria cannot carry out phagocytosis owing to their rigid cell walls, they excrete **exoenzymes** that function outside the cell to degrade large macromolecules. For example, exoenzymes break down proteins and polysaccharides into amino acids and monosaccharides, respectively, which are then transported into the cell for metabolic needs. Protease, DNase, and amylase are examples of exoenzymes (figure 38.1).

Some enzymes are assisted in catalytic reactions by **coenzymes.** The latter transfer small molecules from one molecule to another. For example, the coenzymes NAD$^+$ and FAD transfer protons and coenzyme A transfers acetate groups. Most coenzymes are derivatives of vitamins. As examples, NAD$^+$ is synthesized from niacin, and FAD comes from folic acid. Coenzymes are only required by a cell in catalytic amounts, however, and when an enzymatic reaction catalyzes an oxidation step that converts NAD$^+$ to NADH, the coenzyme must be converted back into its oxidized form if the metabolic pathway is to continue

to function. Many of the reactions that define respiration and fermentation are concerned with regenerating coenzymes such as NAD$^+$ and FAD.

The primary goal of catabolism is the production of energy, which is needed for biosynthesis and growth. Bacteria can obtain their energy needs by two different metabolic means, respiration or fermentation. In respiration, organic molecules are completely degraded to carbon dioxide and water. ATP is generated by the energy created from a proton gradient that is established across the cell membrane when protons are transported from the cytoplasm to the outside of the cell. The shuttling of electrons down an electron transport chain involving cytochromes facilitates the movement of the protons to the outside of the cell. This process is called **oxidative phosphorylation** and, in the process, reduced coenzyme NADH generated in metabolic reactions is converted back to NAD$^+$ because oxygen acts as the terminal electron acceptor and is converted to water. In contrast, fermentation is the partial breakdown of organic molecules to alcohols, aldehydes, acids, and gases such as carbon dioxide and hydrogen. In this process, organic molecules in metabolic pathways serve as terminal electron acceptors and become the end products in a fermentation pathway. Reactions that carry out oxidation steps and utilize NAD$^+$ in metabolic pathways are coupled to reactions that use NADH to reduce the

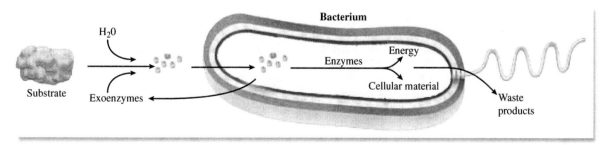

Figure 38.1 Note that the hydrolytic exoenzymes split larger molecules into smaller ones, utilizing water in the process. The smaller molecules are then assimilated by the cell to be acted upon by endoenzymes to produce energy and cellular material.

metabolic intermediates. An example is the oxidation of glyceraldehyde-3-phosphate in glycolysis being coupled with the formation of lactate from pyruvate when *Streptococcus lactis* ferments glucose.

In fermentation, ATP is synthesized by **substrate level phosphorylation** in which metabolic intermediates in pathways directly transfer high-energy phosphates to ADP to synthesize ATP. In the glycolytic fermentation of glucose, ATP is formed when phosphoenol pyruvate transfers a high-energy phosphate to ADP and pyruvate is formed. In general, fermentation is much less efficient in producing energy relative to respiration because the use of metabolic intermediates as electron acceptors leaves most of the available energy in molecules that form the end products. Some bacteria are capable of growing both by respiration and fermentation. *Escherichia coli* is a facultative aerobe that will grow by respiratory means if oxygen is present but will switch metabolic gears in anaerobic conditions and grow by fermentation.

Sugars, particularly glucose, are compounds most widely used by fermenting organisms. However, other compounds such as organic acids, amino acids, and fats are fermented by bacteria. Butter becomes rancid because bacteria ferment butter fat producing volatile and odoriferous organic acids. The end products of a particular fermentation are like a "fingerprint" for an organism and can be used in its identification. For example, *Escherichia coli* can be differentiated from *Enterobacter aerogenes* because the primary fermentation end products for *E. coli* are mixed organic acids, whereas *E. aerogenes* produces acetylmethylcarbinol, a neutral end product.

Tests To Be Performed

Two different kinds of tests will be performed in this exercise: (1) **fermentation tests** to determine if your unknown is capable of carrying out various fermentation reactions and (2) **oxidative tests** to determine if your unknown carries out respiratory metabolism. One test, the O/F glucose test is designed to differentiate between these two modes of metabolism and ascertain if the organism is oxidative, fermentative, or capable of both kinds of metabolism. The fermentation tests to be done are the O/F glucose, specific sugar fermentations, mixed-acid fermentation (methyl red [MR] test), butanediol fermentation (Voges-Proskauer [VP] test), and citrate test (figure 38.2). The oxidative tests to be performed are: the oxidase, catalase, and nitrate tests (figure 38.3). If the O/F glucose test determines

that your organism is oxidative and not capable of fermenting sugars, then your bacterium cannot be identified by fermentation tests, and you will have to rely on other tests to identify your unknown.

The performance of these tests on your unknown may involve a considerable number of inoculations because a set of positive test controls are needed to which you will compare your unknown bacterium (figure 38.4). Although photographs of the various tests are provided this in manual, seeing the actual test results will be much more meaningful. Also keep in mind that some bacteria may not give the same exact results as listed in *Bergey's Manual* as an isolate can often differ from its description in the manual.

As you perform the various tests, attempt to determine which tests may define a specific group of organisms. Some tests may be specific in an identification of an unknown while others may not be specific and therefore not useful in determining the identify of your unknown. Keep in mind that *it is not routine practice to perform all the tests in identifying an unknown.* Although your goal is to identify your unknown, it is also an important for you to learn how to perform the various tests and how to interpret them. The use of an unknown bacterium to identify simply makes it more of a challenge. In actual practice in hospitals and clinical laboratories, biochemical tests are used very selectively. The "shotgun" method of using all the tests is to be avoided because it is wasteful and can lead to confusing results.

Fermentation Tests

First Period

Inoculation should be set up for positive test controls and for your unknown. The media for each set of inoculations are listed separately under each heading.

Unknown Inoculations

The first biochemical test in determining the identity of your organism will be to ascertain whether your organism is oxidative or fermentative. For this, you will inoculate O/F glucose tubes with your unknown, a fermentative and oxidative organism, *Escherichia coli,* and an oxidative organism, *Pseudomonas aeruginosa.*

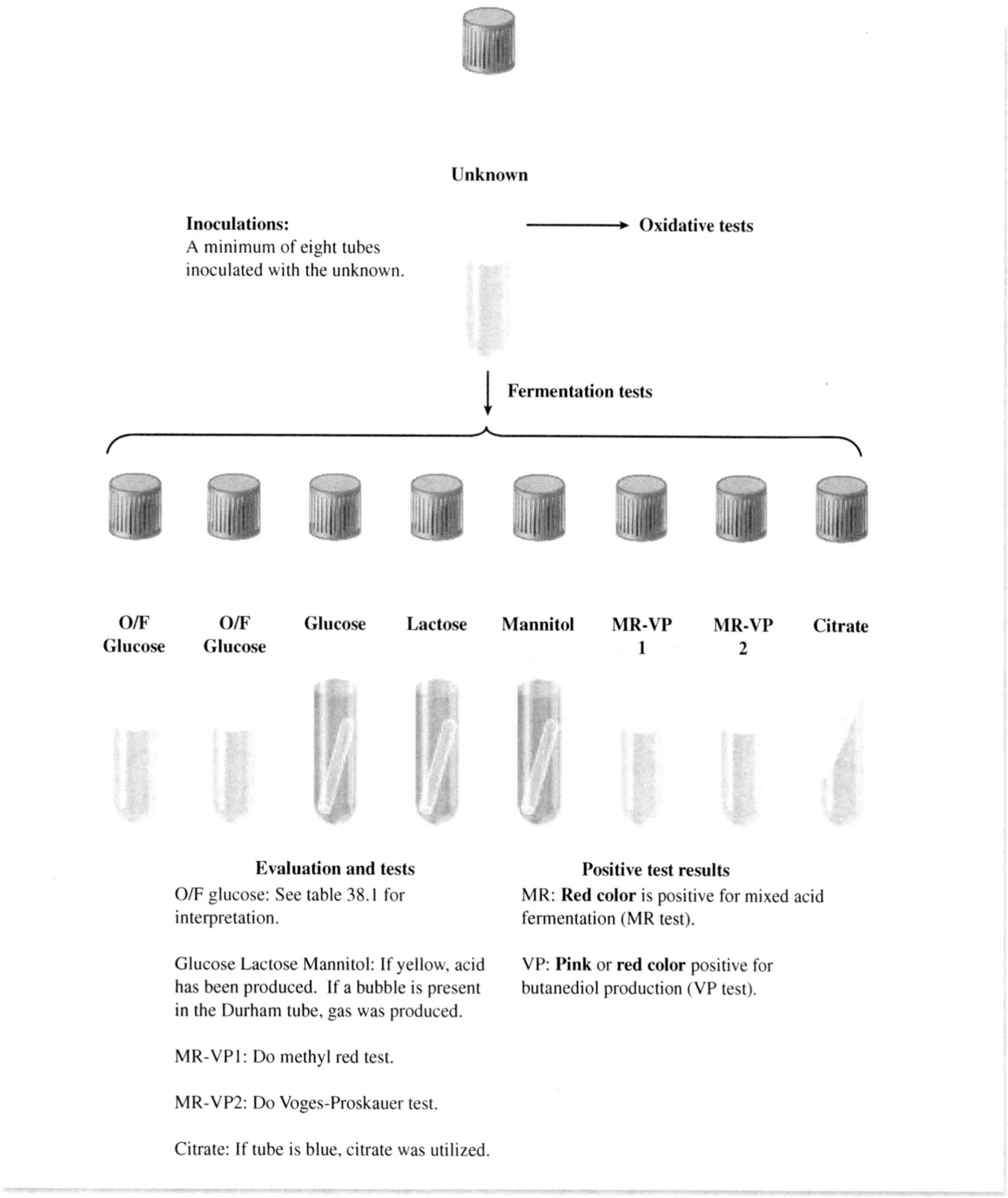

Physiological Characteristics: Oxidation and Fermentation Tests ▌ EXERCISE 38

Unknown

Inoculations:
A minimum of eight tubes
inoculated with the unknown.   ⟶ **Oxidative tests**

↓ **Fermentation tests**

O/F Glucose	O/F Glucose	Glucose	Lactose	Mannitol	MR-VP 1	MR-VP 2	Citrate

Evaluation and tests

O/F glucose: See table 38.1 for
interpretation.

Glucose Lactose Mannitol: If yellow, acid
has been produced. If a bubble is present
in the Durham tube, gas was produced.

MR-VP1: Do methyl red test.

MR-VP2: Do Voges-Proskauer test.

Citrate: If tube is blue, citrate was utilized.

Positive test results

MR: **Red color** is positive for mixed acid
fermentation (MR test).

VP: **Pink** or **red color** positive for
butanediol production (VP test).

Figure 38.2 Procedure for performing fermentation test.

Microbiology, 11th Edition,
Short Version

EXERCISE 38 ▌ Physiological Characteristics: Oxidation and Fermentation Tests

Oxidative Test

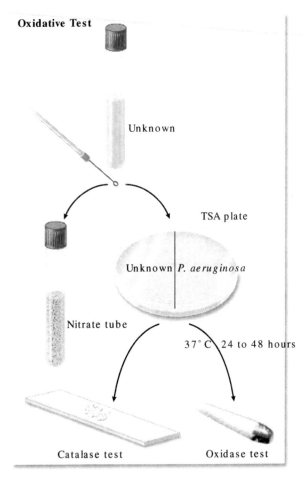

Figure 38.3   Procedure for performing oxidative tests.

Materials

- 6 O/F glucose tubes
- sterile mineral oil

1. Each unknown organism and each test organism will be inoculated into two tubes of O/F glucose by stabbing with an inoculating needle.
2. To one of the tubes for each organism, aseptically deliver about 1 ml of sterile mineral oil after you have inoculated the tube. The mineral oil will establish anaerobic conditions in the tube. The tube without the mineral oil will be aerobic; therefore, be sure to loosen the cap about a quarter of a turn to allow access to the air.
3. Incubate the tubes at 37° C for 24 hours.
4. Record the results and compare them to the data in table 38.1 and the results in figure 38.5. **Note:** If your tubes do not show any color change from the uninoculated control at 24 hours, incubate them for an additional 48 hours and read them again.

Table 38.1   Interpretation of the O/F Glucose Test

Result		Interpretation
ANAEROBIC	AEROBIC	
Yellow	Yellow	Oxidative and fermentative metabolism
Green	Yellow	Oxidative metabolism
Green	Green	Sugar not metabolized (nonsaccharolytic)

Specific Fermentation Reactions

If your organism was found to be fermentative in its metabolism, it will be important to determine which specific sugars are fermented or which fermentation pathways are used for growth. Testing for the fermentation of specific sugars or the end products of fermentation pathways are important phenotypic characteristics used to identify bacteria in *Bergey's Manual*. The following fermentation tests will be studied in this exercise: (1) Durham tube sugar fermentations, (2) mixed-acid fermentation (methyl red test), (3) 2,3-butanediol fermentation (Voges-Proskauer test), and (4) citrate test.

Unknown Inoculations

First Period   Figure 38.2 illustrates the procedure for inoculating the fermentation tests with your unknown. Your instructor may suggest other carbohydrates to be tested, and therefore blanks have been provided in the materials section for this purpose. *Different colored tube caps may be used to distinguish the different carbohydrates and so be sure to record the cap color with the sugars given below.*

Materials: (for each unknown)

- carbohydrate broths with Durham tubes and phenol red indicator with the following sugars:
  1 glucose tube
  1 lactose tube
  1 mannitol tube
- 2 MR-VP broth tubes
- 1 Simmon's citrate tube
- 1 trypticase soy agar (TSA) plate

1. Label each tube with the number of your unknown and an identifying letter as shown in figure 38.2.
2. Label one-half of a TSA plate with your unknown and the other half with *Pseudomonas aeruginosa*. This plate will be used in the next section for oxidative tests to determine if your organism produces the respiratory enzyme, cytochrome oxidase (figure 38.3).

**Microbiology, 11th Edition,
Short Version**

Physiological Characteristics: Oxidation and Fermentation Tests   ▎ EXERCISE 38

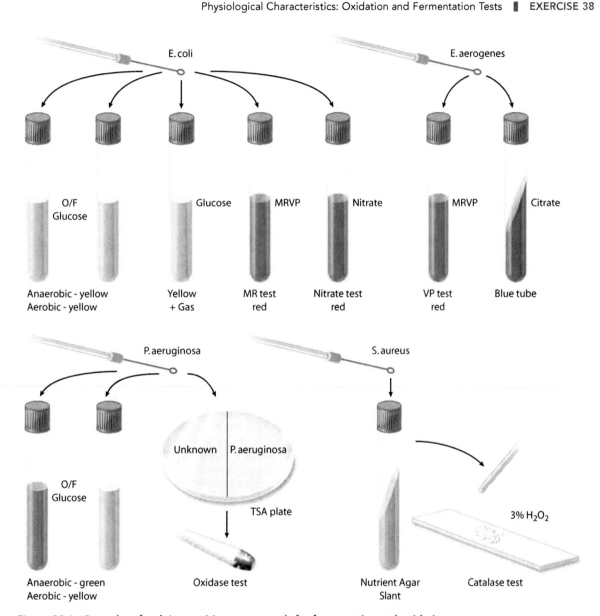

Figure 38.4   Procedure for doing positive test controls for fermentation and oxidative tests

3. Inoculate the Durham sugar tubes and the MR-VP broth tubes with your unknown.
4. Using an inoculating needle, first inoculate the Simmon's citrate slant by streaking the slant, and then stab the center of the slant about three-quarters of the way down into the butt of the tube.
5. Incubate the carbohydrate tubes, the Simmon's citrate tube, and the TSA plate for 24 hours.
6. Incubate the MR-VP broth tubes for 3 to 5 days.

Test Control Inoculations

Figure 38.4 above illustrates the procedure for inoculating the test control tubes.

Materials

- 4 O/F glucose deeps
- 1 glucose broth with Durham tube and phenol red indicator

**Microbiology, 11th Edition,
Short Version**

EXERCISE 38 ▌ Physiological Characteristics: Oxidation and Fermentation Tests

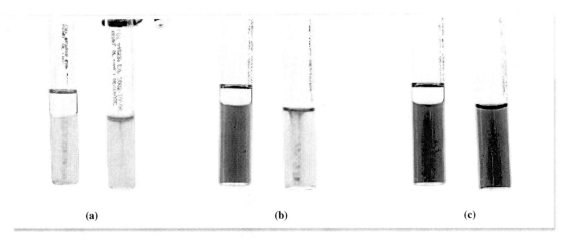

(a)   (b)   (c)

Figure 38.5 O/F glucose test. (a) Fermentative and oxidative; (b) oxidative; (c) glucose not metabolized or inert. © The McGraw-Hill Companies/Auburn University Photographic Services

- 2 MR-VP broth tubes
- 1 Simmon's citrate tube

1. Label each tube with the organism inoculated:

   O/F glucose deeps
   glucose broth
   MR-VP broth
   MR-VP broth
   Simmon's citrate

2. Inoculate each of the test tubes with the appropriate organism as listed.
3. Incubate the glucose tube and the Simmon's citrate tube at 37° C for 24 hours.
4. Incubate the MR-VP broth tubes at 37° C for 3 to 5 days.

Second Period

(Test Evaluations)

After 24 to 49 hours incubation, arrange all your tubes with the unknown tubes in one row and the test controls in another. As you interpret the results, record the information in the descriptive chart on page 243. Do not trust your memory. Any result that is not properly recorded will have to be repeated.

Carbohydrates in Durham Tubes

If an organism ferments a sugar, acid is usually produced, and gas may also be an end product of the fermentation. The presence of acid is indicated by a color change in the pH indicator, phenol red, from red at alkaline pH values to yellow at acidic pH values. The production of gas such as hydrogen and carbon dioxide is revealed by the displacement of medium from the Durham tube (figure 38.6).

Note: Positive gas production should only be recorded when at least 10% of the medium has been displaced from the Durham tube.

Each sugar broth is supplemented with a specific carbohydrate at a concentration of 0.5% as well as beef extract or peptone to satisfy the nitrogen

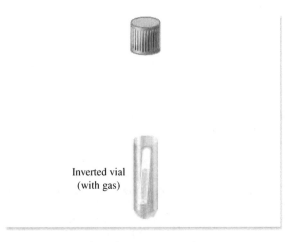

Inverted vial
(with gas)

Figure 38.6 Durham fermentation tube.

Physiological Characteristics: Oxidation and Fermentation Tests   ▌   EXERCISE 38

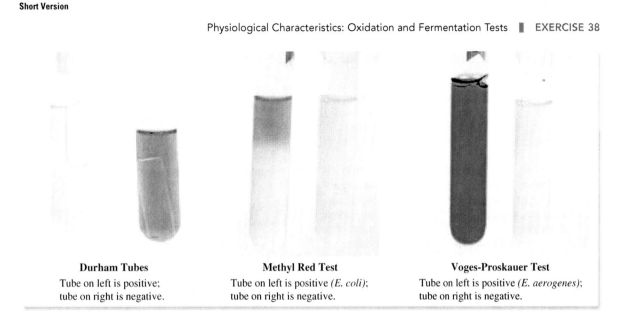

| **Durham Tubes** | **Methyl Red Test** | **Voges-Proskauer Test** |
| Tube on left is positive; tube on right is negative. | Tube on left is positive *(E. coli)*; tube on right is negative. | Tube on left is positive *(E. aerogenes)*; tube on right is negative. |

Figure 38.7   Durham tubes, mixed-acid, and butanediol fermentation tests.
© The McGraw-Hill Companies/Auburn University Photographic Service

requirements of most bacteria. It is reasonable to assume that your unknown may ferment other sugars, but glucose, lactose, and mannitol are reasonable choices to start with as they are important in differentiating some of the medically important bacteria. Your instructor may suggest additional carbohydrates to be tested now or later that will assist in the identification of your organism.

Interpretation of the Results

Examine the glucose tube inoculated with *E. coli.* Note that the phenol red has turned from red to yellow, indicating the presence of acids from the fermentation of the glucose. Also note if medium has been displaced from the Durham tube. If at least 10% of the liquid has been displaced, it means that gas has been formed from the fermentation of the sugar. Figure 38.7 illustrates the difference between a positive and a negative test for both acid and gas production.

Now examine the test tubes with the test sugars, glucose, lactose, and mannitol that you inoculated with your unknown organism. Record the results for acid and gas production, comparing them to the positive control tubes. If there was no color change, record "none" in the descriptive chart. No color change is usually consistent with an oxidative organism. Keep in mind that a negative test result for your unknown is just as important as a positive result.

Mixed-Acid Fermentation
(Methyl Red Test)

An important test in differentiating some of the gram-negative intestinal bacteria is that of mixed-acid fermentation. Genera such as *Escherichia, Salmonella, Proteus,* and *Aeromonas* ferment glucose to produce a number of organic acids such as lactic, acetic, succinic, and formic acids. In addition CO_2, H_2, and ethanol are also produced in this fermentation. The amount of acid produced is sufficient to lower the pH of the MR-VP broth to 5.0 or less.

To test for the presence of these acids, the pH indicator, methyl red, is added to the medium, which turns red if acid is present. A positive methyl red test indicates that the organism has carried out *mixed-acid fermentation.* The bacteria that are mixed-acid fermenters also generally produce gas because they elaborate the enzyme **formic hydrogenlyase,** which splits formic acid to produce CO_2 and H_2.

Medium   MR-VP medium is a glucose broth that is buffered with peptone and dipotassium phosphate.

Test Procedure   Perform the methyl red test first on the control, *E. coli* and then on your unknown.

Microbiology, 11th Edition,
Short Version

EXERCISE 38 ▌ Physiological Characteristics: Oxidation and Fermentation Tests

Materials

• dropping bottle of methy red indicator

1. Add 3–4 drops of methyl red indicator to one of the MR-VP control tubes inoculated with *E. coli*. The tube should become red immediately. A positive tube is shown in the middle illustration of figure 38.7.
2. Repeat this procedure for one of the MR-VP broth tubes inoculated with your unknown organism. If your tube does not become red but remains unchanged (figure 38.7), your unknown is methyl red negative.
3. Record your results in the descriptive chart on page 243.

2,3-Butanediol Fermentation

(Voges-Proskauer Test)

Some of the gram-negative intestinal bacteria do not carry out mixed-acid fermentation, but rather they ferment glucose to produce limited amounts of some organic acids and primarily a more neutral end product, 2,3-butanediol. All species of *Enterobacter* and *Serratia* as well as some species of *Erwinia* and *Aeromonas* carry out the butanediol fermentation. There are also some species of *Bacillus* that produce butanediol when grown on glucose. If an organism produces butanediol and is positive for the Voges-Proskauer (VP) test, it is usually negative for the methyl red test. The methyl red test and the Voges-Proskauer test are important tests for differentiating the gram-negative bacteria.

The neutral end product, 2,3-butanediol, is not detected directly but must be converted to acetoin by oxidation of the 2,3-butanediol. The acetoin reacts with Barritt's reagent, which consists of α naphthol and KOH. The reagent is added to a **3 to 5 day old culture** grown in MR-VP medium and vigorously shaken to oxidize the 2,3-butanediol to acetoin. The tube is allowed to stand at room temperature for 30 minutes, during which time the tube will turn pink to red if acetoin is present (figure 38.7, right illustration).

Test Procedure   Perform the VP test on the control MR-VP broth tube inoculated with *Enterobacter aerogenes* and on the second MR-VP broth tube inoculated with your unknown organism. Follow this procedure:

Materials

• Barritt's reagent
• 2 pipettes (1 ml size)
• 2 empty test tubes

1. Lable one empty test tube for your unknown and the other for *E. aerogenes* (positive control).
2. Pipette 1 ml of culture from your unknown to its respective tube and 1 ml of *E. aerogenes* to its respective tube. Use separate pipettes for each transfer.
3. Add 18 drops (about 0.5 ml) of Barritt's reagent A (alpha-naphthol) to each of the tubes containing 1 ml of culture.
4. Add 18 drops (0.5 ml) of Barritt's reagent B (KOH) to each of the test tubes.
5. Cap or cover the mouth of each test tube and shake the tubes vigorously. Allow the tubes to stand for 30 minutes. In this time, the tube with *E. aerogenes* should turn pink to red. compare this to your unknown. *Vigorous shaking is necessary to oxidize the 2,3-butanediol to acetoin, which reacts with Barritt's reagents to give the red color.*

The left-hand tube in the right-hand illustration of figure 38.7 shows a positive VP result, which is pink to red.

6. Record your results on the descriptive chart on page 243.

Citrate Test

Some bacteria are capable of using citrate as a sole carbon source. Normally citrate is oxidatively metabolized by the Kreb's cycle. However, some bacteria such as *Enterobacter aerogenes* and *Salmonella thyphimurium* can cleave citrate to produce oxaloacetate and pyruvate. These intermediates are then fermented to produce several end products such as formate, acetate, lactate, acetoin, and CO_2. The medium also contains ammonium salts that serve as a sole nitrogen source for growth. Organisms degrading citrate must also use the ammonium salts, and in the process, they produce ammonia that causes the medium to become alkaline. Under alkaline conditions, the pH indicator in the medium turns from dark green to a deep Prussian blue, indicating the utilization of citrate.

Materials

• Simmon's citrate tubes

1. Label one tube of Simmon's citrate with *Enterobacter aerogenes* and another tube with your unknown number. Using an inoculating needle, first streak the surface of the slant and then stab the needle into the middle of the slant.
2. Incubate the tubes with *E. aerogenes* and your unknown at 37° C for 24 to 48 hours.

Physiological Characteristics: Oxidation and Fermentation Tests ▌ EXERCISE 38

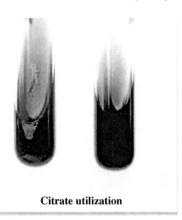

Citrate utilization

Figure 38.8 Left-hand tube exhibits citrate utilization (Prussian blue color). Right-hand tube is uninoculated or negative (green).
© The McGraw-Hill Companies/Auburn University Photographic Services

3. Examine the slants. The slant inoculated with *E. aerogenes* will be a deep Prussian blue because the organism has utilized citrate. Compare this tube to your unknown. If the tube for your unknown has remained green, citrate was not utilized (figure 38.8).
4. Record your results in the descriptive chart.

Oxidative Tests (Refer to Figure 38.3)

Oxidase Test

The oxidase test assays for the presence of cytochrome oxidase, an enzyme in the electron transport chain. This enzyme catalyzes the transfer of electrons from reduced cytochrome *c* to molecular oxygen, producing oxidized cytochrome *c* and water. Cytochrome oxidase occurs in bacteria that carry out respiration where oxygen is the terminal electron acceptor; hence, the test differentiates between those bacteria that have cytochrome oxidase and use oxygen as a terminal electron acceptor from those that can use oxygen as a terminal electron acceptor but have other types of terminal oxidases. The enzyme is detected by the use of an artificial electron acceptor, N,N,N',N'-tetramethyl-*p*-phenylenediamine, which changes from yellow to purple when electrons are transferred from reduced cytochrome *c* to the artificial acceptor.

The oxidase test will differentiate most species of oxidase-positive *Pseudomonas* from the Enterobacteriaceae, which are oxidase negative. The artificial acceptor is somewhat unstable and can oxidize if left exposed to air for prolonged periods of time. In this exercise, you will use a commercially prepared reagent stored in glass ampules that are broken just prior to use.

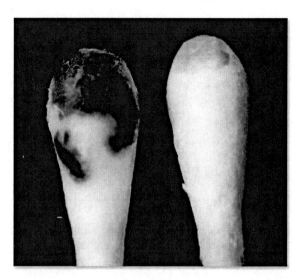

Figure 38.9 Left-hand swab shows a purple reaction due to oxidase production. Right-hand swab shows a culture that is oxidase negative.
© The McGraw-Hill Companies/Auburn University Photographic Service

Materials

- TSA plate streaked with your unknown on one-half and *Pseudomonas aeruginosa* streaked on the other half (figure 38.3).
- ampule of 1% oxidase reagent, N,N,N',N'-tetramethyl-*p*-phenylenediamine dihydrochloride (Difco)
- Sterile swabs
- Whatman no. 2 filter paper

1. Grasp an ampule of oxidase reagent between your thumb and forefinger. Hold the ampule so that it is pointed away from you and squeeze the ampule until the glass breaks. Tap the ampule gently on the tabletop several times.
2. Touch a sterile swab to the growth of *Pseudomonas aeruginosa* on the TSA plate. Deliver several drops of oxidase reagent to the cells on the swab. (**Note:** You do not have to remove the cap of the oxidase reagent as it has a small hole for delivery of the reagent.)
   Alternatively: Transfer growth from the TSA plate to a piece of filter paper and add several drops of reagent to the cells on the paper.
3. A positive culture will cause the reagent to turn from yellow to purple in 10 to 30 seconds. A change after 30 seconds is considered a negative reaction (figure 38.9).
4. Repeat the test procedure for your unknown organism and record the results in the descriptive chart.

Catalase Test

When aerobic bacteria grow by respiration, they use oxygen as a terminal electron acceptor, converting it to water. However, they also produce hydrogen

EXERCISE 38 ▌ Physiological Characteristics: Oxidation and Fermentation Tests

peroxide as a by-product of this reaction. Hydrogen peroxide is a highly reactive oxidizing agent that can damage enzymes, nucleic acids, and other essential molecules in the bacterial cell. To avoid this damage, aerobes produce the enzyme **catalase,** which degrades hydrogen peroxide into harmless oxygen and water.

$$2H_2O_2 \xrightarrow{\text{catalase}} 2H_2O + O_2$$

Strict anaerobes and aerotolerant bacteria such as *Streptococcus* lack this enzyme, and hence they are unable to deal with the hydrogen peroxide produced in aerobic environments. The presence of catalase is one way to differentiate these bacteria from aerobes or facultative aerobes, both of which produce catalase. For example, catalase production can be used to differentiate aerobic staphylococci from streptococci and enterococci, which lack this enzyme.

Test Procedure   To determine if catalase is produced, a small amount of growth is transferred from a plate or slant, using a wooden stick, to a clean microscope slide. A couple of drops of 3% hydrogen peroxide are added to the cells on the slide. If catalase is produced, there will be vigorous bubbling due to the breakdown of hydrogen peroxide and the production of oxygen gas.

   Note: Do not use a wire loop to transfer and mix the cells as iron can cause the hydrogen peroxide to break down, releasing oxygen. Also, do not perform the catalase test on cells growing on blood agar since blood contains catalase.

Materials

- 3% hydrogen peroxide
- nutrient agar slant tube with *Staphylococcus aureus* and your unknown on the TSA plate

1. Using the end of a wooden swab, transfer some cells from the *S. aureus* culture to the surface of a clean microscope slide.
2. Add 2 to 3 drops of 3% hydrogen peroxide to the cells, mix with the wooden stick, and observe for vigorous bubbling (figure 38.4).
3. Repeat the same procedure for your test organism and record your results in the descriptive chart.

Nitrate Reduction

Some facultative anaerobes can use nitrate as a terminal electron acceptor in a type of anaerobic respiration called **nitrate respiration.** Bacteria such

as *Paracoccus* and some *Pseudomonas* and *Bacillus* reduce nitrate to a gaseous end products such as N_2O or N_2. Other bacteria such as *Escherichia coli* partially reduce nitrate to nitrite. Several enzymes are involved in the reduction of nitrate, one of which is nitrate reductase, which catalyzes the transfer of electrons from cytochrome *b* to nitrate, reducing it to nitrite. The enzymes involved in nitrate reduction are inducible and are only produced if nitrate is present and anaerobic conditions exist for growth. The chemical reaction for the reduction of nitrate to nitrite is as follows:

$$NO_3^- + 2e^- + 2H^+ \xrightarrow{\text{nitrate reductase}} NO_2^- + H_2O$$

Test Procedure   The ability of bacteria to reduce nitrate can be determined by assaying for the end products of nitrate reduction: gas or nitrite. Cultures are grown in beef extract medium containing potassium nitrate. Gases produced from nitrate reduction are captured in Durham tubes placed in the nitrate medium. Partial reduction of nitrate to nitrite is assayed for by adding sulfanilic acid (reagent A) followed by dimethyl-alpha-naphthylamine (reagent B). If nitrite is produced by reduction, it will form a chemical complex with the sulfanilic acid and the dimethyl-alpha-naphthylamine to give a dark red color (figure 38.10). A negative test could mean that nitrate was not reduced or that a some other reduced form nitrogen was produced, such as ammonia or hydroxlyamine. As a check, zinc powder is added to the test medium. Zinc metal will chemically reduce nitrate to nitrite, causing the medium to turn dark red as result of the formation of the chemical complex. If a nongaseous product such as ammonia was produced, no color will develop after the addition of the zinc metal.

Materials

- nitrate broth cultures with Durham tubes of the unknown organism and the test control *E. coli*
- nitrate test reagents: reagent A—sulfanilic acid; reagent B—dimethyl-alpha-naphthylamine
- zinc powder

1. Examine the nitrate broth of your unknown. If gas has been displaced in the Durham tube, it means that your organism has reduced nitrate to a gaseous end product, such as nitrogen gas. If no gas is present, reduction may have resulted in the formation of nitrite or the formation of a nongaseous end product.

Physiological Characteristics: Oxidation and Fermentation Tests   ▌ EXERCISE 38

Figure 38.10 Nitrate test: Left-hand tube shows red color due to nitrate reduction. Middle tube shows reduction of nitrate to nitrogen gas that is trapped in the Durham tube. Right tube is an uninoculated control.
© The McGraw-Hill Companies/Auburn University Photographic Service

1. To test for the presence of nitrite, first assay the test control *E. coli* culture by adding 2 to 3 drops of reagent A and 2 to 3 drops of reagent B to the nitrate broth culture of the organism. A deep red color will develop immediately (figure 38.10).

> **CAUTION:** Avoid skin contact with solution B. Dimethyl-alpha-naphthylamine is carcinogenic.

2. Repeat this same test procedure for your unknown bacterium. If a red color fails to appear, your organism did not reduce nitrate or it may have produced a nongaseous end product of nitrate reduction.

   Zinc Test: To the negative culture, add a pinch of zinc powder and shake the tube vigorously. If a red color develops in the tube, nitrate was reduced by the zinc metal, indicating a negative test for nitrate reduction. If no color develops, a nongaseous end product may have been formed, which means your unknown reduced nitrate.

3. Record your results in the Laboratory Report 38–40.

Physiological Characteristics:
Hydrolytic and Degradative Reactions

39

exercise

Because bacteria have a rigid cell wall, they are unable to surround and engulf their food by the process of phagocytosis, which is characteristic of higher cells. To acquire nutrients, bacteria excrete a variety of hydrolytic and degradative exoenzymes that degrade large macromolecules into smaller units that can be transported into the cell for metabolic purposes. For example, amylases and cellulases degrade starch and cellulose, respectively, into simple sugars that are then transported into the cell where they are metabolized by fermentation or oxidation. A variety of proteases degrade proteins, such as casein and gelatin, and polypeptides into amino acids. Triglycerides are degraded into fatty acids and glycerol by various lipases. Sometimes bacteria also hydrolyze small molecules because they can thereby acquire carbon compounds for metabolic purposes. For example, tryptophane is split into pyruvate and indole by the enzyme tryptophanase. The pyruvate is metabolized, but the indole ring accumulates in the growth medium because it cannot be broken down. The accumulation of indole is the basis for a biochemical test that differentiates bacteria that produce trytophanase from those that do not produce the enzyme. Some bacteria hydrolyze urea to produce carbon dioxide and ammonia, thereby causing the pH to become alkaline. The change in pH is detected by a color change in a pH indicator. *Proteus* and other bacteria can oxidatively deaminate phenylalanine to produce phenylpyruvic acid. The latter can be detected with ferric chloride.

The presence of various hydrolytic and degradative enzymes can be used as a basis for identifying bacteria. In this exercise, you will perform biochemical tests for detecting hydrolytic and degradative reactions carried out by bacteria. In each case, you will compare your unknown to reactions carried out by test control organisms.

First Period

(Inoculations)

If each student is working with only one unknown organism, students can work in pairs to share petri plates. Note in figure 39.1 how each plate can serve for two unknowns and a test control organism streaked down the middle of the plate. If each student is working with two unknowns, the plate should not be shared. Whether or not materials will be shared will depend on the availability of materials.

Materials

per pair of students with one unknown each or for one student with two unknowns:
- 1 starch agar plate
- 1 skim milk agar plate
- 1 spirit blue agar plate
- 3 urea slants or broths
- 3 tryptone broths
- phenylalanine agar
- nutrient broth cultures: *Bacillus subtilis, Escherichia coli, Staphylococcus aureus,* and *Proteus vulgaris*

1. Label and streak the three different agar plates as shown in figure 39.1. Note that straight line streaks are made on each plate. Indicate, also, the type of medium in each plate.
2. Label a urea slant or urea broth tube with *P. vulgaris* and a tryptone broth tube with *E.coli*. These are the test control tubes for urea and tryptophan hydrolysis, respectively. Inoculate each with the respective organism.
3. For each unknown, label one urea slant or broth and one tryptone tube with the code number of your unknown. Inoculate each tube with your unknown.
4. Label one phenylalanine agar slant with your unknown number and a second slant with *P. vulgaris.* Inoculate each slant with the respective organism.
5. Incubate the test control cultures at 37° C. Incubate the unknowns at the optimum temperatures that you determined for them.

Second Period

(Evaluation of Tests)

After 24 to 48 hours incubation, compare your unknown and test controls, recording all data on the descriptive charts on page 243.

Starch Hydrolysis

The starch macromolecule consists of two constituents: (1) amylose, a straight chain polymer of 200 to 300 glucose molecules and (2) amylopectin, a larger branched polymer of glucose. Bacteria that hydrolyze starch produce *amylases* that degrade the starch molecule into molecules of maltose, glucose, and dextrins.

**Microbiology, 11th Edition,
Short Version**

EXERCISE 39 ▌ Physiological Characteristics: Hydrolytic and Degradative Reactions

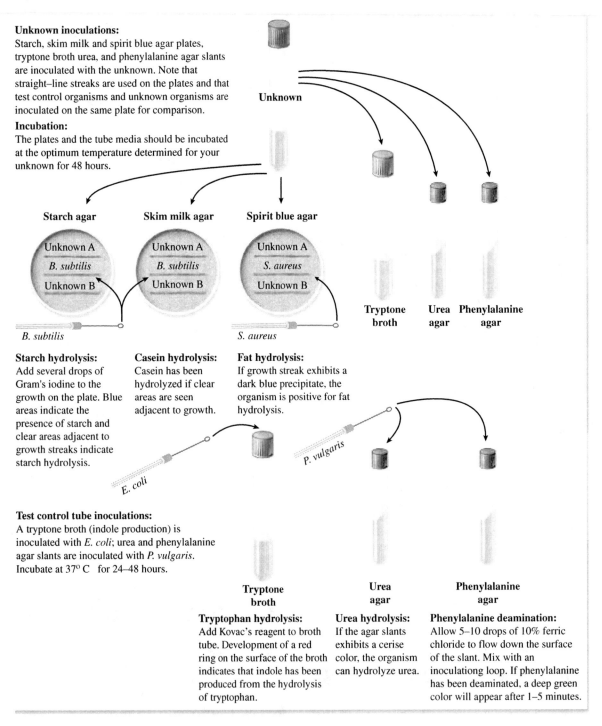

Unknown inoculations:
Starch, skim milk and spirit blue agar plates, tryptone broth urea, and phenylalanine agar slants are inoculated with the unknown. Note that straight–line streaks are used on the plates and that test control organisms and unknown organisms are inoculated on the same plate for comparison.

Incubation:
The plates and the tube media should be incubated at the optimum temperature determined for your unknown for 48 hours.

Starch hydrolysis:
Add several drops of Gram's iodine to the growth on the plate. Blue areas indicate the presence of starch and clear areas adjacent to growth streaks indicate starch hydrolysis.

Casein hydrolysis:
Casein has been hydrolyzed if clear areas are seen adjacent to growth.

Fat hydrolysis:
If growth streak exhibits a dark blue precipitate, the organism is positive for fat hydrolysis.

Test control tube inoculations:
A tryptone broth (indole production) is inoculated with *E. coli*; urea and phenylalanine agar slants are inoculated with *P. vulgaris*. Incubate at 37° C for 24–48 hours.

Tryptophan hydrolysis:
Add Kovac's reagent to broth tube. Development of a red ring on the surface of the broth indicates that indole has been produced from the hydrolysis of tryptophan.

Urea hydrolysis:
If the agar slants exhibits a cerise color, the organism can hydrolyze urea.

Phenylalanine deamination:
Allow 5–10 drops of 10% ferric chloride to flow down the surface of the slant. Mix with an inoculationg loop. If phenylalanine has been deaminated, a deep green color will appear after 1–5 minutes.

Figure 39.1   Procedure for doing hydrolysis tests on unknowns

Starch hydrolysis is detected by adding iodine to starch medium. Iodine complexes with the starch macromolecule and causes the medium to turn blue. However, if the starch has been degraded, the medium adjacent to the bacterial growth will be clear after the addition of the iodine.

Physiological Characteristics: Hydrolytic and Degradative Reactions   ▌ EXERCISE 39

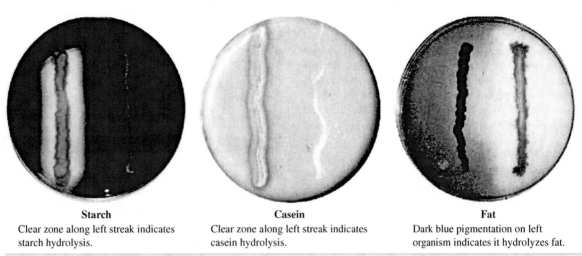

Starch	Casein	Fat
Clear zone along left streak indicates starch hydrolysis.	Clear zone along left streak indicates casein hydrolysis.	Dark blue pigmentation on left organism indicates it hydrolyzes fat.

Figure 39.2   Hydrolysis test plates: Starch, casein, fat.

Materials

- Gram's iodine
- starch agar plates with test control organism and your unknown

1. Pour enough Gram's iodine over the surface of the starch plate to cover the entire plate. Rotate and tip the plate to spread the iodine. *Bacillus subtilis* produces amylases that degrade starch. If starch is degraded, a clear area will occur next to the growth of the organism. Areas on the plate where no starch hydrolysis has occurred will be blue.
2. Compare your unknown on the same plate to *B. subtilis*. Figure 39.2 illustrates a positive starch hydrolysis result.
3. Record your results.

Casein Hydrolysis

Casein is the predominant protein in milk, and its presence causes milk to have its characteristic white color. Many bacteria produce *proteases,* which are enzymes that degrade protein molecules such as casein into peptides and amino acids. This process is referred to as *proteolysis.*

Examine the growth on the skim milk agar. Note the **clear zone** surrounding *B. subtilis* where proteolysis of the casein has occurred. Figure 39.2 illustrates casein hydrolysis. Compare your unknown to *B. subtilis.* Record the results on the descriptive chart on page 243.

Fat Hydrolysis

Fats or triglycerides are composed of a glycerol molecule to which fatty acid molecules are covalently bonded

through ester bonds. Triglycerides are primarily fat storage products in higher organisms such as animals. Some bacteria produce enzymes called *lipases* that cleave the fatty acids from glycerol. The fatty acids and glycerol can then be used for metabolic purposes such as synthesizing phospholipids for membrane construction or for catabolism to produce energy. The decomposition of triglycerides and the breakdown of the fatty acids into short chain volatile organic acids is the reason why butter or margarine becomes rancid.

$$
\begin{array}{ccc}
CH_2\!-\!O\!-\!\overset{\displaystyle O}{\overset{\|}{C}}\!-\!R & & CH_2OH + RCOOH \\[2pt]
| & & | \\[2pt]
CH\!-\!O\!-\!\overset{\displaystyle O}{\overset{\|}{C}}\!-\!R' \xrightarrow[\text{lipase}]{+\,3\,H_2O} & & CHOH + R'COOH \\[2pt]
| & & | \\[2pt]
CH_2\!-\!O\!-\!\overset{\displaystyle O}{\overset{\|}{C}}\!-\!R'' & & CH_2OH + R''COOH \\[6pt]
\text{Triglyceride} & \text{Glycerol} & \text{Fatty acids}
\end{array}
$$

Spirit blue agar contains peptone as a source of carbon, nitrogen, and vitamins. It also contains tributyrin, a simple, natural animal triglyceride that serves as a substrate for lipases. Release of the fatty acids from tributyrin via lipase activity results in the lowering of the pH of the agar to produce a **dark blue precipitate.** However, some bacteria do not completely hydrolyze all the fatty acids from the tributyrin, and as a result, the pH is not sufficiently lowered to give the dark blue precipitate. In this case, all you notice may be simply the depletion of fat or oil droplets in the agar to indicate lipase activity.

Microbiology, 11th Edition,
Short Version

EXERCISE 39 ▌ Physiological Characteristics: Hydrolytic and Degradative Reactions

Examine the growth of *S. aureus* on the plate. You should be able to see the dark blue reaction as shown in figure 39.2. Compare this to your unknown. *If your unknown appears negative, hold the plate up toward the light and look for a region near the growth where oil droplets are depleted.* If you see the depletion of oil droplets, record this as a positive test in the descriptive chart.

Tryptophan Degradation

Some bacteria have the ability to degrade the amino acid tryptophan producing indole, ammonia, and pyruvic acid. The pyruvic acid can then be used by an organism for various metabolic purposes. The enzyme responsible for the cleavage of tryptophan is *tryptophanase.* The degradation of tryptophan by the enzyme can be detected with Kovac's reagent, which forms a deep red color if indole is present. Tryptone broth (1%) is used for the test because it contains high amounts of tryptophan. Tryptone is derived from casein by a pancreatic digestion of the protein.

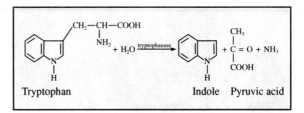

Materials

- Kovac's reagent
- tryptone broth cultures of *E. coli* and your unknown

To test for indole and therefore the activity of tryptophanase, add 10 to 12 drops of Kovac's reagent to the tryptone broth culture of *E. coli.* A red organic layer should form on top of the culture as shown in figure 39.3. Repeat the test for your unknown culture and record the results on the descriptive chart.

Urea Hydrolysis

Urea is a waste product of animal metabolism that is broken down by a number of bacteria. The enzyme responsible for urea hydrolysis is *urease,* which splits the molecule into carbon dioxide and ammonia. Urease is produced by some of the gram-negative enteric bacteria such as *Proteus, Providencia,* and *Morganella,* which can be differentiated from other gram-negative enteric bacteria by this test. Refer to the separation outline in figure 41.2.

Urea medium contains yeast extract, urea, a buffer, and the pH indicator phenol red. Urea is unstable and is broken down by heating under steam pressure at 15 psi. Therefore, the medium is prepared by adding filter-sterilized urea to the base medium after autoclaving it.

When urease is produced by an organism, the resulting ammonia causes the pH to become alkaline. As the pH increases, the phenol red changes from yellow (pH 6.8) to a bright pink or cerise color (pH 8.1 or greater). See figure 39.4.

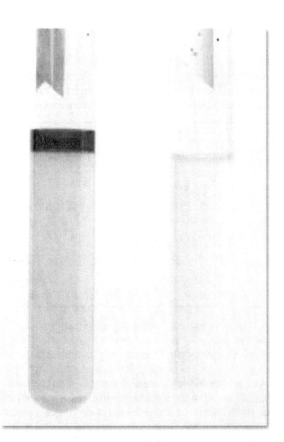

Figure 39.3 Tryptophan hydrolysis. The left tube shows the presence of indole (red band) at the top of the tube. The right-hand tube is an uninoculated control.
© The McGraw-Hill Companies/Auburn University Photographic Service

Examine the urea slant inoculated with *Proteus vulgaris* and compare it to your unknown. *If your urea slant is negative, continue the incubation for an additional 7 days to check for slow urease production.* Record your results in the descriptive chart on page 243.

Microbiology, 11th Edition,
Short Version

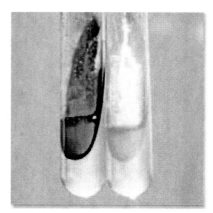

PPA test

Figure 39.5   Left-hand tube exhibits a positive reaction (green). Other tube is negative.

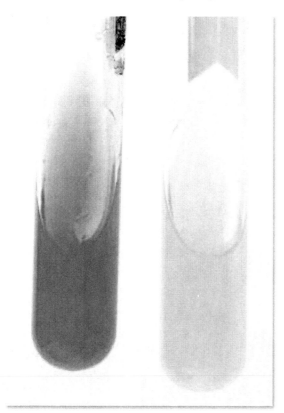

Figure 39.4   Urease test. Tube on the left is positive (*Proteus*); tube on the right is negative.
© The McGraw-Hill Companies/Auburn University Photographic Service

Phenylalanine Deamination

Gram-negative bacteria such as *Proteus, Morganella,* and *Providencia* can oxidatively deaminate the amino acid phenylalanine to produce phenylpyruvic acid and ammonia. The reaction is catalyzed by the enzyme *phenylalanine deamninase,* a flavoprotein oxidase.

The enzyme can be detected by the addition of 10% ferric chloride, which forms a green colored complex with α-keto acids such as phenylpyruvic acid. The test is useful in differentiating the above bacteria from other Enteriobacteriaceae.

Materials

- dropping bottle of 10% ferric chloride

Allow 5 to 10 drops of 10% ferric chloride to flow down the slant of the test control organism, *P. vulgaris.* To facilitate the reaction, use an inoculating loop to emulsify the culture on the slant with the test reagent. A deep **green color** should appear in 1 to 5 minutes. Refer to figure 39.5. Repeat the test procedure for your unknown. Record your results in the Laboratory Report.

Physiological Characteristics:
Multiple Test Media

Some media are designed to give multiple test results. These include: Kligler's iron agar, which determines fermentation reactions for glucose and lactose and the production of hydrogen sulfide; SIM, which determines hydrogen sulfide and indole production and motility; and litmus milk, which detects fermentation, proteolysis, and other reactions in milk. In addition, the IMViC tests will be discussed; these are an important group of tests used in differentiating some gram-negative enteric bacteria.

First Period

(Inoculations)

As before, test control cultures are included in this exercise. For economy of materials, one set of test control cultures will be made by students working in pairs.

Materials

for test control cultures, per pair of students:
* 1 Kligler's iron agar deep
* 3 SIM deeps
* nutrient broth cultures of *Proteus vulgaris*, *Staphylococcus aureus*, and *Escherichia coli* for each unknown per student
* 1 Kligler's iron agar slant
* 4 SIM deeps
* 1 Litmus milk tube

1. Label one tube of Kligler's iron agar with *P. vulgaris* and additional tubes with your unknown numbers. Inoculate each tube by swabing and then stabbing with an inoculating loop.
2. Label the SIM deeps with *P. vulgaris, S. aureus, E. coli,* and your unknown number.
3. Label one tube of litmus milk with your unknown number. (**Note:** A test control culture for litmus milk will not be made. Interpretation of results will be made based on figure 40.3.)
4. Incubate the test control cultures at 37° C and the unknown cultures at their optimum temperatures for 24 to 48 hours.

Second Period

(Evaluation of Tests)

After the 24 to 48 hours of incubation, examine the tubes and evaluate the results based on the following

discussion. Record the test results in the descriptive chart.

Kligler's Iron Agar

Kligler's iron agar is a multiple test medium that will detect the fermentation of glucose and lactose and the production of hydrogen sulfide resulting from the breakdown of the amino acid cysteine. It contains 0.1% glucose, 1% lactose, peptone, ferrous salts, and phenol red as a pH indicator. It is prepared as a slant and is inoculated by streaking the slant and stabbing the butt of the tube. The medium is useful in the differentiation of the gram-negative enteric bacteria.

Fermentation Reactions

The following are the possible results for the fermentation of the carbohydrates in the medium (see figure 40.1 A–C).

1. Alkaline (red) slant/acid (yellow) butt: This means that only glucose was utilized. The organism utilized the low concentration of glucose initially and then degraded the peptone in the medium. The slant is alkaline (red) because glucose was degraded aerobically, and the ammonia released from peptone utilization caused the aerobic slant to become alkaline. However, the butt is yellow (acid) because glucose was fermented anaerobically to produce enough acids to cause the acidic reaction in the butt. If gas is produced, it will be evident by the splitting of the medium and the formation of gas bubbles in the agar slant.
2. Acid (yellow) slant/acid (yellow) butt: The organism has fermented both glucose and lactose, producing acids that cause the pH indicator to turn yellow. Lactose is present in ten times (1%) the concentration of glucose (0.1%), and sufficient acid is produced to cause both the slant and butt to be acidic. However, the tubes must be read at 24 hours because they can revert to alkaline in 48 hours if the lactose becomes depleted and the peptones are utilized, producing ammonia.
3. Alkaline (red) slant/alkaline (red) butt; alkaline (red) slant/no change butt: No fermentation of

Microbiology, 11th Edition,
Short Version

EXERCISE 40   ▌ Physiological Characteristics: Multiple Test Media

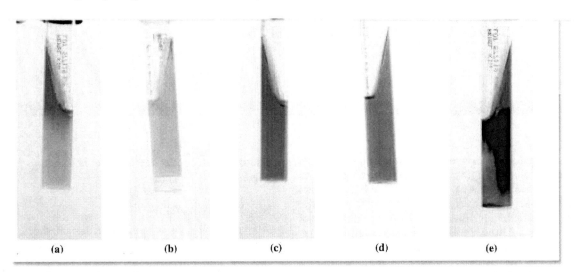

Figure 40.1   Fermentation reactions and hydrogen sulfide production on Kligler's iron agar. (a) Alkaline/ alkaline; (b) acid/acid with gas; (c) alkaline/no change; (d) uninoculated; (e) hydrogen sulfide production.
© The McGraw-Hill Companies/Auburn University Photographic Service

either sugar has occurred. Some enteric bacteria can use the peptones both aerobically and anaerobically, causing both the slant and butt to become alkaline. Others can only use the peptone aerobically, producing an alkaline slant but no change in the butt.

Hydrogen Sulfide

Bacteria such as *Proteus vulgaris* can degrade the amino acid cysteine to produce pyruvic acid, ammonia, and hydrogen sulfide. The initial step in the reaction pathway is the removal of sulfide from cysteine, which is catalyzed by *cysteine desulfurase*. This enzyme also requires the coenzyme pyridoxal phosphate for activity.

$$
\begin{array}{c}
\text{CH}_2 \cdot \text{SH} \\
| \\
\text{CH} \cdot \text{NH}_2 + \text{H}_2\text{O} \\
| \\
\text{COOH} \\
\\
\text{Cysteine}
\end{array}
\xrightarrow{\text{Cysteine desulfurase}}
\begin{array}{c}
\text{CH}_3 \\
| \\
\text{C}=\text{O} + \text{H}_2\text{S}\uparrow + \text{NH}_3 \\
| \\
\text{COOH} \\
\\
\text{Pyruvic   Hydrogen Ammonia} \\
\text{acid   sulfide} \\
\text{gas}
\end{array}
$$

Kligler's iron agar contains ferrous salts that will react with the hydrogen sulfide liberated by cysteine desulfurase to produce an insoluble black precipitate, ferrous sulfide. **Note:** Bacteria such as *Proteus* that produce sulfide can obscure the fermentation reaction in the butt of the tube. If sulfide is produced, an acid reaction has occurred in the butt even if it cannot be observed.

Examine the Kligler's iron agar and record the results for the slant and butt of the tubes for the test organisms. Compare the results to your unknown. *Proteus* will produce hydrogen sulfide and cause the tube butt to turn black (figure 40.1 E). Record your results in the descriptive chart.

SIM Medium

SIM medium is a multiple test medium that detects the production of hydrogen sulfide and indole and that determines if an organism is motile or not. The medium contains hydrolyzed casein, ferrous salts, and agar (0.7%), which makes the medium semisolid. It is inoculated by stabbing. The breakdown of tryptophan in the medium will produce indole, which can be detected by adding Kovac's reagent. If cysteine is degraded, hydrogen sulfide will be released, which will combine with the ferrous salts to produce a black precipitate in the tube.

Because the medium contains a low concentration of agar (0.7%), bacteria that are motile are able to swim in the medium. Motility is determined by diffuse growth out from the line of inoculation or by turbidity throughout the tube. In contrast, non-motile bacteria, such as *Staphylococcus aureus,* will only grow along the line of inoculation (figure 40.2 C, right).

Examine the tubes with control bacteria. *E. coli* is motile and will therefore cause the tube to be turbid (figure 40.2 C, left). Adding Kovac's reagent to the top of the tube results in a red ring, indicating the presence of indole (figure 40.2 B). The SIM tube inoculated with *P. vulgaris* has a black precipitate due to the production of hydrogen sulfide (figure 40.2 A).

Physiological Characteristics: Multiple Test Media   ▌ EXERCISE 40

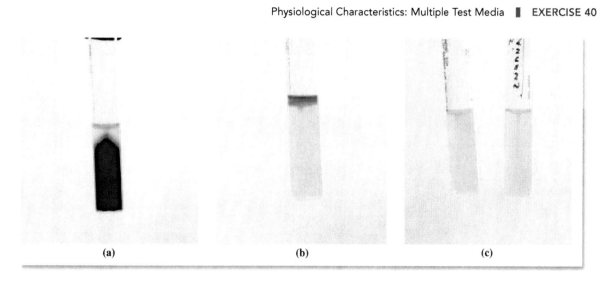

Figure 40.2   Reactions on SIM medium. (a) Hydrogen sulfide production; (b) indole production; (c) motility, left tube, motile organism, versus right tube, non-motile organism.
© The McGraw-Hill Companies/Auburn University Photographic Service

Compare these results with those of your unknown and record them in the descriptive chart.

The IMViC Tests

Sometimes a grouping of tests can be used to differentiate organisms. For example, *E. coli* can be differentiated from *E. aerogenes* by comparing four tests collectively called the IMViC (*I*: indole test; *M*: methyl red test; *V*: Voges-Proskauer test; and *C*: citrate test) tests. The results for the two organisms appear below. The two bacteria give exactly opposite reactions for the tests.

	I	M	V	C
E. coli	+	+	−	−
E. aerogenes	−	−	+	+

These two bacteria are very similar in morphological and physiological characteristics. The IMViC tests can be valuable when testing water for sewage contamination because they can rule out *E. aerogenes*, which is not always associated with sewage.

If your organism is a gram-negative rod and a facultative anaerobe, group these tests and see how your organism fits the combination of tests.

Litmus Milk

Litmus milk contains 10% powdered skim milk and the pH indicator litmus. The medium is adjusted to pH 6.8 and has a purplish blue color before in-oculation. Milk contains the proteins casein, lactalbumin, and lactogloblin as well as the disaccharide lactose, and they provide an excellent growth medium for many microorganisms. Bacteria that ferment the lactose, resulting in acid production, will cause the litmus to turn pink. Other bacteria digest the milk proteins using proteases. This results in the release of ammonia, causing the litmus to turn purple because of the alkaline condition. Some of the proteolytic bacteria can also cause the milk proteins to precipitate and coagulate, thus forming a clot. Clotting can occur because of the production of acid or because of the release of the enzyme *rennin* that converts casein to paracasein.

Certain facultative bacteria can cause the reduction of the litmus dye to a colorless or leuco form. The color change is due to a drop in oxygen levels in the tube that accompanies the production of acids. The reduction of litmus can also occur when bacteria use the dye as an alternative electron acceptor. In these cases, the litmus is acting as a oxidation-reduction indicator as well as a pH indicator.

Figure 40.3 indicates the various color changes and reactions in litmus milk. It should be noted that some of the reactions take 4 to 5 days to fully develop, and therefore cultures should be incubated for this period of time. However, it is important to check the cultures every 24 hours for changes.

Litmus Milk Reactions

Alkaline Reaction   Litmus turns purple or blue because of an alkaline pH produced by the release of ammonia. This can occur in the first 24 hours of incubation and is typical of proteolytic bacteria.

Microbiology, 11th Edition,
Short Version

EXERCISE 40 ▌ Physiological Characteristics: Multiple Test Media

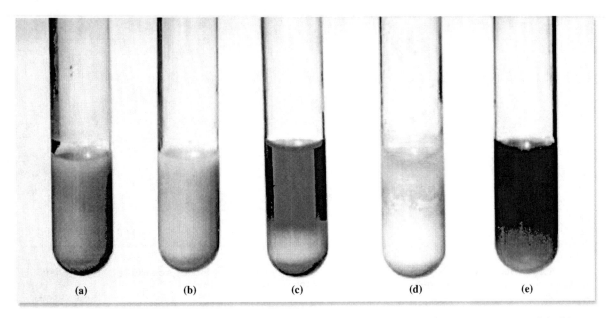

Figure 40.3 Litmus milk reactions: (a) Alkaline. (b) Acid. (c) Upper transparent portion is peptonization; solid white portion in bottom is coagulation and litmus reduction; overall redness is interpreted as acid. (d) Coagulation and litmus reduction in lower half; some peptonization (transparency) and acid in top portion. (e) Litmus indicator is masked by production of soluble pigment (*Pseudomonas*); some peptonization is present but difficult to see in photo.

Acid Reaction Litmus turns pink owing to acidic conditions, which is typical of bacteria that ferments the milk sugar.

Litmus Reduction The culture becomes white because the litmus dye is reduced due to a drop in oxygen levels in the culture or because the dye has been reduced as a result of bacteria using it as an alternative electron acceptor.

Coagulation Curd formation can result from the precipitation and coagulation of proteins. Tilting the tube 45° will confirm whether or not coagulation has occurred.

Peptonization The medium becomes translucent, often turning brown at this stage. This is characteristic of proteolytic bacteria that degrade milk proteins.

Ropiness The formation of a thick slime in the culture that can be demonstrated by inserting a sterile loop and carefully withdrawing it from the culture. The slime will adhere to the loop, forming strings.

Record the results of the litmus milk reactions for your unknown on the descriptive chart on page 243.

Laboratory Report

Complete the Laboratory Report 38–40, which summarizes all the physiological tests performed on your unknown in the last three exercises.

Physiological Characteristics of Bacteria (continued)

13. In addition to the morphological, cultural, and physiological tests performed on an unknown, what tests can be conducted to further assist in its identification?

_____

_____

C. Matching Questions

1. *MEDIA.* Match the name of the medium with the physiological test. A media may be used more than once. Tests may require more than one answer.

   a. Kligler's iron agar
   b. MR-VP broth
   c. phenol red lactose
   d. SIM medium
   e. Simmon's citrate agar
   f. skim milk agar
   g. spirit blue agar
   h. tryptone broth

   _____   2,3-butanediol fermentation
   _____   carbohydrate fermentation
   _____   casein hydrolysis
   _____   citrate utilization
   _____   hydrogen sulfide production
   _____   mixed-acid fermentation
   _____   triglyceride hydrolysis
   _____   tryptophan degradation

2. *REAGENTS.* Match the name of the reagent with the physiological test. Tests may require more than one answer.

   a. alpha-naphthol
   b. dimethyl-alpha-naphthylamine
   c. ferric chloride
   d. Gram's iodine
   e. hydrogen peroxide
   f. Kovac's reagent
   g. methyl red
   h. N,N,N',N'-tetramethyl-p-phenylenediamine dihydrochloride
   i. potassium hydroxide
   j. sulfanilic acid

   _____   2,3-butanediol fermentation
   _____   catalase test
   _____   mixed-acid fermentation
   _____   nitrate reduction

Microbiology, 11th Edition,
Short Version

Physiological Characteristics of Bacteria (continued)

_____ oxidase test

_____ phenylalanine deamination

_____ starch hydrolysis

_____ tryptophan degradation

3. _ENZYMES_. Match the name of the enzyme with the biochemical reaction. Enzymes may be used more than once.

   a. amylase

   b. cysteine desulfurase

   c. lipase

   d. protease

   e. tryptophanase

   f. urease

_____ casein hydrolysis

_____ gelatin liquefaction

_____ hydrogen sulfide production

_____ indole

_____ starch hydrolysis

_____ triglyceride hydrolysis

_____ urea hydrolysis

4. _PRODUCTS_. Match the name of the product with the biochemical reaction. Products may be used more than once. Tests may require more than one answer.

   a. 2,3-butanediol

   b. ammonia

   c. fatty acids

   d. indole

   e. molecular oxygen

   f. phenylpyruvic acid

_____ catalase

_____ phenylalanine deamination

_____ triglyceride hydrolysis

_____ tryptophan degradation

_____ urea hydrolysis

_____ Voges-Proskauer test

Reading References

General Information

Alcamo, I. Edward. *Fundamentals of Microbiology,* 7th ed. Reading, Mass.: Addison-Wesley, 2001.

Atlas, R. M., and Bartha, R. *Microbial Ecology: Fundamentals and Applications,* 4th ed. Menlo Park, Calif.: Benjamin/Cummings Publishing, 1997.

Baron, Samuel, ed. *Medical Microbiology,* 4th ed. Reading, Mass.: Addison-Wesley, 1996.

Brock, Thomas D. *Robert Koch: A Life in Medicine and Bacteriology.* Herndon, Va.: ASM Press, 2000.

Brogden, Kim A., et al. *Virulence Mechanisms of Bacterial Pathogens,* 3rd ed. Herndon, Va.: ASM Press, 2000.

Brun, Yves V., and Shimkets, L. J. *Prokaryotic Development.* Herndon, Va.: ASM Press, 2000.

Burlage, Robert S., Atlas, R., Stahl, D., Geesey, G., and Saylor, G. *Techniques in Microbial Ecology.* Cary, N.C.: Oxford University Press, 1998.

Chan, Pelczar, and Krieg. *Laboratory Exercises in Microbiology,* 6th ed. New York: McGraw-Hill, 1993.

Collier, Leslie H., et al. *Topley and Wilson's Microbiology and Microbial Infections.* Six Volumes. Herndon, Va.: ASM Press, 1998.

Colwell, Rita R. *Nonculturable Microorganisms in the Environment.* Herndon, Va.: ASM Press, 2000.

Doyle, Michael P., et al. *Food Microbiology: Fundamentals and Frontiers.* Herndon, Va.: ASM Press, 2001.

Dubos, Rene. *Pasteur and Modern Science.* Paperback. Herndon, Va.: ASM Press, 1998.

Flint, S. J., et al. *Principles of Virology: Molecular Biology, Pathogenesis, and Control of animal viruses,* 2nd-ed. Herndon, Va.: ASM Press, 2003.

Gerhardt, Philipp, et al. *Methods for General and Molecular Bacteriology.* Herndon, Va.: ASM Press, 1994.

Hurst, Christon J., et al. *Manual of Environmental Microbiology,* 2nd ed. Herndon, Va.: ASM Press, 2002.

Karam, Jim D., et al. *Molecular Biology of Bacteriophage T-4.* Herndon, Va.: ASM Press, 1994.

Lacey, Alan J. *Light Microscopy in Biology,* 2nd ed. Cary, N.C.: Oxford University Press, 1999.

Lederberg, Joshua, et al. *Encyclopedia of Microbiology.* New York: Academic Press, 1997.

Lovley, Derek R. *Environmental Microbe-Metal Interactions.* Herndon, Va.: ASM Press, 2000.

Madigan, Michael T., and Marrs, Barry L. *Extremophiles.* New York: Scientific American Vol. 276, Number 4: pp. 82–87, 1997.

Madigan, Michael T., Martinko, John M., and Parker, Jack. *Brock Biology of Microorganisms,* 11th ed. Englewood Cliffs, N.J.: Prentice-Hall, 2005.

Mobley, Harry L. T., and Warren, John W. *Urinary Tract Infections.* Herndon, Va.: ASM Press, 1995.

Needham, Cynthia, et al. *Intimate Strangers: Unseen Life on Earth.* Herndon, Va.: ASM Press, 2000.

Prescott, Lansing M., Harley, John P., and Klein, Donald A. *Microbiology,* 6th ed. New York: McGraw-Hill, 2005.

Rose, Noel R. *Manual of Clinical Laboratory Immunology,* 6th ed. Herndon, Va.: ASM Press, 2002.

Rosenburg, Eugene. *Microbial Ecology and Infectious Disease.* ASM Press, 1999.

Salyers, Abigail A., and Whitt, D. D. *Bacterial Pathogenesis,* 2nd ed. Herndon, Va.: ASM Press, 2001.

Smith, A. D., et al. *Oxford Dictionary of Biochemistry and Molecular Biology.* Cary, N.C.: Oxford University Press, Revised ed. 2000.

Snyder, Larry, and Champness, Wendy. *Molecular Genetics of Bacteria,* 2nd ed. Herndon, Va.: ASM Press, 2002.

Talaro, K., and Talaro, A. *Foundations in Microbiology,* 5th ed. Dubuque, IA; New York: McGraw-Hill, 2005.

Tortora, Gerard J., Funke, B. R., and Case, C. L. *Microbiology: An Introduction,* 8th ed. Menlo Park, Calif.: Benjamin/Cummings Publishing, 2003.

Walker, Graham C., and Kaiser, Dale. *Frontiers in Microbiology: A Collection of Minireviews from the Journal of Bacteriology.* Herndon, Va.: ASM Press, 1993.

White, David. *The Physiology and Biochemistry of Prokaryotes,* 2nd ed. Cary, N.C.: Oxford University Press, 1999.

Laboratory Procedures

American Type Culture Collections. *Catalog of Cultures,* 8th ed. Rockville, Md. www.atcc.org

Atlas, R. M., and Snyder, J. W. *Handbook of Media for Clinical Microbiology.* Boca Raton, Fla.: CRC Press, 1996.

Chart, Henrik. *Methods in Practical Laboratory Bacteriology.* Boca Raton, Fla.: CRC Press, 1994.

Difco Laboratory Staff. *Difco Manual of Dehydrated Culture Media and Reagents,* 11th ed. Detroit, Mich.: Difco Laboratories, 1998.

Flemming, D. O., Richardson, J. H., Tulis, J. J., and Vesley, D. *Laboratory Safety: Principles and Practices,* 2nd ed. Herndon, Va.: ASM Press, 1995.

Garcia, Lynne S., and Brukner, David A. *Diagnostic Medical Parasitology,* 4th ed. Herndon, Va.: ASM Press, 2001.

Isenberg, Henry D., et al. *Clinical Microbiology Procedures Handbook,* Vols. 1 and 2, 2nd ed. Herndon, Va.: ASM Press, 2004.

MacFaddin, Jean *Biochemical Tests for Identification of Medical Bacteria,* 3rd ed. Lippincott Williams & Wilkins NY.-1999.

Miller, Michael J. *A Guide to Specimen Management in Clinical Microbiology,* 2nd ed. Herndon, Va.: ASM Press, 1999.

Murray, Patrick R., et al. *Manual of Clinical Microbiology,* 8th ed. Herndon, Va.: ASM Press, 2003.

Murray, Patrick R., et al. *Manual of Clinical Microbiology,* 7th ed. Herndon, Va.: ASM Press, 1999.

Shapton, D. A., and Shapton, N. F. *Principles and Practices of Safe Processing of Food.* New York: Academic Press, 1994.

Identification of Microorganisms

Fischetti, Vincent A., et al. *Gram-Positive Pathogens.* Herndon, Va.: ASM Press, 2000.

Holt, John G., Kreig, N. R., et al. *Bergey's Manual of Systematic Bacteriology,* vol. 1, 1st ed. Baltimore, Md.: Williams & Wilkins, 1984.

Jahn, Theodore L., et al. *Protozoa,* 2nd ed. Dubuque, Ia.: WCB/McGraw-Hill, 1978.

Lapage, S. P., et al. *International Code of Nomenclature of Bacteria.* Herndon, Va.: ASM Press, 1992.

Larone, Davise. *Medically Important Fungi: A Guide to Identification,* 4th ed. Herndon, Va.: ASM Press, 2002.

Murray, Patrick, et al. *Manual of Clinical Microbiology,* 8th-ed. Bethesda, Md.: American Society for Microbiology, 2003.

Piggot, Patrick J., et al. *Regulation of Bacterial Differentiation.* Herndon, Va.: ASM Press, 1993.

Skerman, V. B. D., and Sneath, P. H. A. *Approved Lists of Bacterial Names.* Herndon, Va.: ASM Press, 1998.

Sneath, Peter H. A., et al. *Bergey's Manual of Systematic Bacteriology,* vol. 2, 1st ed. Baltimore, MD.: Williams & Wilkins, 1986.

Staley, James T., et al. *Bergey's Manual of Systematic Bacteriology,* vol. 3, 1st ed. Baltimore, MD.: Williams & Wilkins, 1989.

Sanitary and Medical Microbiology

Balows, Albert et al. *Manual of Clinical Microbiology,* 5th ed. Herndon, Va.: ASM Press, 1991.

Flemming, D. O., Richardson, J. H., Tulis, J. J., and Vesley, D. *Laboratory Safety: Principles and Practices,* 2nd ed. Herndon, Va.: ASM Press, 1995.

Greenberg, Arnold E., et. al. *Standard Methods for the Examination of Water and Wastewater,* 19th ed. Washington, D.C.: American Public Health Association, 1995.

Jay, James M. *Modern Food Microbiology,* 6th ed. New York: Chapman-Hall, 2000.

Kneip, Theodore, and Crable, John V. *Methods for Biological Monitoring: A Manual for Assessing Human Exposure to Hazardous Substances.* Washington, D.C.: American Public Health Association, 1988.

Marshall, Robert T. *Standard Methods for the Examination of Dairy Products,* 16th ed. Washington, D.C.: American Public Health Association, 1992.

Miller, Michael J. *A Guide to Specimen Management in Clinical Microbiology,* 2nd ed. Herndon, Va.: ASM Press, 1998.

Ray, Bibek. *Fundamental Food Microbiology,* 3rd ed. Boca Raton, Fla.: CRC Press, 2003.

Vanderzant, Carl, and Splittstoesser, Don. *Compendium of Methods for the Microbiological Examination of Foods,* 3rd ed. Washington, D.C.: American Public Health Association, 1992.

Microbiology, 11th Edition,
Short Version

Index

Microbiology, 11th Edition,
Short Version

INDEX

Microbiology, 11th Edition,
Short Version

Microbiology, 11th Edition,
Short Version

INDEX

**Microbiology, 11th Edition,
Short Version**

INDEX

INDEX

**Microbiology, 11th Edition,
Short Version**

INDEX

Microbiology, 11th Edition,
Short Version

INDEX

INDEX

**Microbiology, 11th Edition,
Short Version**

INDEX

Microbiology, 11th Edition,
Short Version

INDEX

CPSIA information can be obtained
at www.ICGtesting.com
Printed in the USA
EDOW021611130613
1897ED

MGH0000008204